WEIGHT, *Diet* and BODY *Image*

Edward Abramson, PhD
Author of *It's NOT Just Babyfat!*

Copyright © 2016 by Edward Abramson, PhD

Published by:
PESI Publishing & Media
PESI, Inc
3839 White Ave
Eau Claire, WI 54703

Cover: Amy Rubenzer
Editing: Donald Altman
Layout: Bookmasters & Amy Rubenzer

ISBN: 9781683730286

Proudly printed in the United States of America

www.pesipublishing.com

For
Jeremy, Annie & Sam, Bessie and Isaac
— you guys rock!

Table of Contents

Introduction. xi

Chapter One
How Heavy Is Too Heavy? 1

Chapter Two
Why Gaining Is Easy But Losing Is Hard 13

Chapter Three
Diets, Drugs, Supplements and Surgery: What Works? 21

Chapter Four
Why Are You Eating That? – Physical Hunger 37

Chapter Five
Why Are You Eating That? – External Cues 47

Chapter Six
Why Are You Eating That? – Emotions. 57

Chapter Seven
Why Are You Eating That? – Relationships. 71

Chapter Eight
Why Is It So Hard To Get Active? – Exercise. 81

Chapter Nine
Body Image. 93

Chapter Ten
The Obesity Epidemic: Personal Responsibility
or Toxic Environment? 103

Chapter Eleven
A Treatment Program 111

Chapter Twelve
Childhood Obesity 123

Preface

I confess, I may be fixated at the oral stage. Although I'm not a big fan of psychoanalytic theorizing, this could be one possible explanation for my career-long interest in both normal and pathological eating. Ever since the late 1960s when I stumbled upon Stanley Schachter's pioneering research on eating in the absence of hunger I've been hooked, trying to figure out why people eat and how to help them when their eating causes problems. This book contains much of what I've learned.

This book would not have been possible without the input from hundreds of people who, over the years, have shared their struggles with eating and weight with me. A few of their stories, highly disguised, are presented in the following pages. To all of them, a hearty thank you!

I also need to acknowledge the contributions of friends and colleagues who provided useful information, helpful advice, or just thoughtful listening. Linda Jackson of PESI Publishing & Media and Donald Altman made many valuable suggestions while Dr. Kris Picklesheimer, Dr. Bob Schoen, Harris Miller, and Elizabeth Herzberg were supportive throughout the process of writing this book.

Edward Abramson, PH.D. is a licensed clinical psychologist, Professor Emeritus at California State University, Instructor at U. C. Berkeley Extension, and former Director of the Eating Disorders Center at Chico Community Hospital. He is the author of five books and more than 20 scientific studies of obesity and eating disorders.

Dr. Abramson has appeared on dozens of television and radio programs including *20/20, Hard Copy,* and *Joan Rivers.* He is routinely quoted in publications including *NY Times, Good Housekeeping, O, The Oprah Magazine, Washington Post,* and *Us Weekly.* Ed is a Fellow of the Obesity Society and served on the Board of Directors of the California Psychological Association.

Ed writes a blog, *It's NOT Just Babyfat!* for *Psychology Today Magazine* and lectures to professional and lay audiences throughout the U.S., Canada, and Europe. He gets enthusiastic reviews as an engaging speaker who combines an extensive knowledge of research on eating issues with clinical insight gained from years of professional experience. He makes his home in Oakland, California and enjoys his Sonoma coast retreat and motorcycle adventures in the U.S. and overseas.

Introduction

You may know the stats; two thirds of all Americans are overweight or obese. You're probably aware that the obesity epidemic presents serious problems — everything from increased risk of diabetes and cardiovascular disease to the estimated quarter of a billion dollars it costs for the extra jet fuel airlines need to carry their overweight passengers. What is less obvious is that, if you're a mental health clinician, nurse, physician, occupational therapist, dietitian, personal trainer, or other professional, many of your clients, regardless of their diagnosis or presenting problem, are concerned about their weight.

Even if your clients aren't in a formal weight loss program or consulting you for an eating disorder their weight concerns may play a critical role in their treatment. Medical problems ranging from sleep apnea to back pain to stroke may be affected by excess weight. Psychological difficulties including depression, marital conflict, and self-esteem issues frequently include a weight component. Issues such as body dissatisfaction, health risks associated with obesity, or concerns about their children's eating and weight may emerge in your work with your client.

It's not uncommon for clients to want to know *THE* cause of their weight gain, but there rarely is a single cause. Diets, supplements, or programs often oversimplify and claim to have the solution to your clients' weight concerns. Although it would be easier if there were a single determinant of weight, everything from genetics, to brain function, physiology, emotions, relationships, culture, economics, politics, and even urban planning play a role in how much anyone will weigh. Given this complexity, how are you going to address your client's concerns? How can you help them resolve, or at least understand, their weight issues?

This book is designed to do just that. It's a guide to help you approach weight issues with clients. This is a handbook that can help you answer a client's questions with solid information and the latest research to back it up. Most importantly, this book will help you make sense out of all the conflicting information about diets, weight, and exercise. The media, including TV programs, magazines, and web sites, is full of reports revolving around these issues. The information in these pages will give you a solid base from which to answer client's questions, as well as to explore more deeply their beliefs about diet and weight, and how this may affect the medical or psychological issues you are treating.

While there are many excellent books for therapists working with eating disordered clients, this book offers an overview of the processes that determine weight without delving too deeply in the technical aspects or methodology of the research findings. It will provide the basic information you need to offer realistic help to your clients. If you want to follow-up with the original research the references are provided within each chapter. Keep in mind that obesity is a complex condition and treating it often requires medical consultation and working with a team so it's important to avoid recommendations outside of your scope of practice.

How To Use This Book

Although it is tempting to scan the table of contents and then immediately go to the chapter that deals with an issue that you find particularly relevant, the regulation of weight is complicated so you'll need to review the information in other chapters. For example, bariatric surgery is discussed in Chapter 3 but if your client is considering surgery you'll need to discuss the some of the information dealing with physical activity that is presented in Chapter 8. So, while you may want to skip around, make sure that you go back and read the chapters that you've missed.

How Heavy Is Too Heavy?

Chapter 1 explores the stigma associated with obesity and the effects that stigma has on clients and healthcare providers. It also includes several methods for assessing obesity and reviews controversies about the health risks of being overweight.

Why Gaining is Easy, But Losing is Hard

Chapter 2 presents evidence that, contrary to popular belief, obesity is not just a matter of "willpower." It will show how humans have evolved to have many overlapping mechanisms to conserve energy which, when combined with our current environment, make it easy to gain but hard to lose weight.

Diets, Drugs, Supplements and Surgery: What Works?

Chapter 3 presents the methods most commonly used to lose weight. The dieting controversies will be discussed along with meal replacements, commercial weight loss programs, medications, supplements, web-based programs, and surgical procedures. Outcome research will be briefly reviewed.

Why Are You Eating That? – Physical Hunger

Surprisingly, most eating is not a result of being deprived of food. This chapter includes questions your clients can ask to determine if their desire to eat is a result of true physical hunger. Chapter 4 also explores the effects of sleep deprivation and offers non-dieting suggestions for coping with hunger while minimizing calories.

Why Are You Eating That? – External Cues

There are so many environmental prompts that trigger eating, often without awareness. Several ingenious studies have demonstrated that simple changes in the environment result in either more or less eating. Chapter 5 includes suggestions to help your client become aware of these cues and then change their environment to reduce eating, without feeling deprived.

Why Are You Eating That? – Emotions

Chapter 6 offers suggestions to help your clients determine if some of their eating is a response to emotional arousal. Although binge eating is widely recognized as a feature of eating disorders, less intense forms of emotional eating cause unnecessary weight gain and frequently are responsible for dieting relapse. This chapter includes a questionnaire you can use to help your clients identify their unique pattern of emotional eating and offers alternative methods for dealing with emotions without eating.

Why Are You Eating That? – Relationships

Relationships, especially marriage, can have a huge impact on both gaining and losing weight. Chapter 7 will examine gender differences in weight control and shows how your clients can navigate the hidden sexual and relationship issues that can promote weight gain and make weight loss difficult.

Why Is It So Hard To Get Active? – Exercise

While it's unlikely that exercise, by itself, will result in significant weight loss, research shows that increased physical activity is necessary for weight loss maintenance regardless of how the weight was lost. This chapter describes the common reasons overweight clients resist physical activity and offers practical suggestions to help your clients become more active.

Body Image

Body Image is a frequently overlooked aspect of weight control. While treatments of eating disorders often address body image concerns, obesity treatments usually neglect this important topic. A negative body image — hating the way you look — is not helpful while having a positive body image doesn't lessen motivation to lose weight and improves the quality of life regardless of weight. Chapter 9 includes ideas for assessing and improving your client's body image.

The Obesity Epidemic: Personal Responsibility or Toxic Environment?

Chapter 10 puts weight struggle in a larger context. While your clients may not be able to change the media, government policies, or urban planning, you can help them recognize how these forces affect their weight. This should reduce some of the shame and self-stigma associated with obesity.

A Treatment Program

This chapter presents invaluable information to help your clients lose weight. It includes questions to assess readiness to make the effort required to lose weight as well as suggestions for realistic goal setting. Chapter 11 then provides specific methods for tailoring a cognitive-behavioral program for your client.

Childhood Obesity

Providing direct treatment to children directly is unlikely to be helpful as putting a child on a diet frequently results in weight gain. On the other hand, you can show parents how to use the methods described in this chapter to help their kids get to a healthy weight.

Note on Pronoun Use: To be fair, "he or she" should be used since both men and women are affected by obesity and often have the same issues, but "he or she" is cumbersome. Instead, either pronoun will be used when there aren't sex differences. If there are sex differences, these will be described with the appropriate pronoun. Also, the term "client" will be used to refer to people you might be helping. If you work in a medical setting you can substitute "patient."

Chapter 1

How Heavy Is Too Heavy?

Whenever I'm giving a workshop and use the word "fat" someone in the audience will cringe visibly. The stigma and shame associated with the word is sufficient to elicit a physical response. As we'll see, the word fat doesn't just connote adipose tissue (the technical term for fat) but rather a constellation of personal and moral failings that have resulted in a body that is considered shameful and unattractive.

Unfortunately the shame associated with fat is counterproductive – it makes it more difficult to effectively control weight. One of the first goals in working with weight-conscious clients is to decrease the shame associated with obesity. Becoming comfortable with the word, fat is a good starting point.

Let's look at the terminology we've been using. When I was a child "husky" was a euphemism for fat boys. Husky has gone out of fashion but we have dozens of other terms to describe people who have bodies that are considered to be large. Words such as full-figured, big-boned, heavyset, Rubenesque, etc. enable us to avoid using the term fat. Parts of the body in which fat tissue accumulates are frequently described as bubble butts, love handles, beer bellies, thunder thighs or other "humorous" terms. Some of these terms are nonsensical. For example, big boned suggests that an individual's weight is a result of their bone structure yet bones account for less than 10 percent of body weight. Even if the bones were huge it wouldn't explain anyone's obesity.

Why is it necessary to come up with all these terms that have the sole purpose of allowing us to avoid saying, "fat"?

WHY IS OBESITY SHAMEFUL?

If you're going to be working with clients who've been struggling with their weight it's important to understand the effects of the shame and stigma they've experienced.[1] For example, at work overweight people earn less than normal weight people in comparable positions, get fewer promotions, and are viewed

1

as lazy, less competent, and lacking in self-discipline by their co-workers. In schools, teachers view overweight students as untidy, more emotional, and less likely to succeed in their studies.

The anti-obesity stigma can also affect close interpersonal relationships. One study found that men were more likely to respond to a personal ad for a woman with a history of drug problems than to an ad for an obese woman.[2] Another study of over 2000 overweight and obese women found that 72 percent reported that family members teased them, called them pejorative names, and made negative comments about their weight.[3]

Even when they seek medical care obese individuals are often viewed as lazy, lacking in self-control, weak-willed, sloppy, and dishonest. Interestingly, the negative view of obesity in healthcare settings goes both ways. A recent study found that patients were less inclined to follow medical advice and more likely change providers if the doctor was overweight or obese.[4] Weight bias in healthcare isn't limited to physicians. One study of nurses found that 24 percent were "repulsed" by obese patients.[5] In another study psychologists were found to attribute more pathology, more severe symptoms, and a worse prognosis to obese patients compared with thinner patients presenting similar profiles.[6]

If you harbor negative feelings about overweight people you've got plenty of company. Even a noted humanistic psychiatrist wasn't immune to fat phobia. In his best-selling book, *Love's Executioner,* Dr. Irvin Yalom described his feelings about a fat patient,

> *I have always been repelled by fat women. I find them disgusting: their absurd sidewise waddle, their absence of body contour-breasts, laps, buttocks, shoulders, jawlines, cheekbones, everything, everything I like to see in a woman, obscured in an avalanche of flesh. . .How dare they impose that body on the rest of us?*[7]

Despite these feelings Dr. Yalom was able to get past his initial revulsion and work with this patient. He developed a therapeutic relationship and helped her while becoming more compassionate and understanding of people with eating and weight issues. Towards the end of therapy Dr. Yalom's patient revealed that she knew from the start that he had been repelled by her looks. There's a lesson for everyone who works with this population: it's important to examine your own feelings about fat. Can you get past the stigma of obesity so that you can be helpful to your client?

Given the negative characteristics ascribed to overweight individuals and the rejection they encounter in various settings, they may react to stigma by internalizing the harmful characteristics attributed to them. Since it is widely believed that weight loss is merely a matter of "will power" many overweight people will accept that they are deficient because they've failed at dieting. This is not only counter productive, but it's also irrational since "will power" is only one of the many determinants of weight and dieting might not be the best strategy for weight loss.

The medical and psychological consequences of internalizing weight stigma are profound, and may include:

- Depression
- Binge eating
- Lowered self-esteem
- Body dissatisfaction
- Avoidance of physical activity

In addition, the psychological stress brought on by weight stigma may result in higher blood pressure and increase cardiovascular reactivity resulting in negative health consequences.

The Weight Self-stigma Questionnaire

If you are working with a client with weight concerns it would be useful to determine the effects of stigma on your client. The Weight Self-stigma Questionnaire[8] is a measure intended to identify individuals who have a negative self-evaluation, are ashamed about their weight, and have experienced discrimination based on their weight. Responses to the 12 questions yield an overall score and two subscales: self-devaluation, and fear of being stigmatized or discriminated against. If you are concerned about your own weight it would be useful to complete the questionnaire to see if weight stigma has influenced your thinking.

THE WEIGHT SELF-STIGMA

For each item select the number that best represents how you feel about your weight

1	2	3	4	5
Strongly disagree	Disagree	Neither agree or disagree	Agree	Strongly agree

I'll always go back to being overweight. _____

I caused my weight problems._____

I feel guilty because of my weight problems. _____

I became overweight because I'm a weak person. _____

I would never have any problems with weight if I were stronger. _____

I don't have enough self-control to maintain a healthy weight. _____

I feel insecure about others' opinions of me. _____

People discriminate against me because I've had weight problems. _____

It's difficult for people who haven't had weight problems to relate to me. _____

Others will think I lack self-control because of my weight problems. _____

People think that I am to blame for my weight problems. _____

Others are ashamed to be around me because of my weight. _____

The first six statements measure self-devaluation while the remainder measure fear of being stigmatized. Although there aren't extensive norms there are several possible uses for the questionnaire. Before treatment you could explore your client's response to the items that they agreed or strongly agreed to. This could open a productive discussion that would suggest a focus for your work on her weight issues. Also, you could re-administer the questionnaire at the end of treatment since it has been shown to be sensitive to change. Helping your client overcome the shame of being overweight will be a prerequisite to successful treatment.

UNDERSTANDING BODY MASS INDEX

When should an individual be concerned about his or her weight? For many years the standard was the height-weight tables originally developed by a life insurance company in the 1920's. While they have been updated, the tables are difficult to use and probably not representative of the total population.

Currently, the most widely used method to determine if someone is too heavy is the Body Mass Index (BMI). It's used as a simple measure of how much an individual's weight deviates from what is considered "normal" or desirable for his height. It is calculated by dividing weight in kilos by height in meters squared. You don't need to do the arithmetic, an online BMI calculator is available at www.nhlbi.nih.gov or you can use the following chart to determine your BMI.

BMI	19	20	21	22	23	24	25	26	27	28	29	30	31	32	33	34	35
Height (inches)								**Body Weight (pounds)**									
58	91	96	100	105	110	115	119	124	129	134	138	143	148	153	158	162	167
59	94	99	104	109	114	119	124	128	133	138	143	148	153	158	163	168	173
60	97	102	107	112	118	123	128	133	138	143	148	153	158	163	168	174	179
61	100	106	111	116	122	127	132	137	143	148	153	158	164	169	174	180	185
62	104	109	115	120	126	131	136	142	147	153	158	164	169	175	180	186	191
63	107	113	118	124	130	135	141	146	152	158	163	169	175	180	186	191	197
64	110	116	122	128	134	140	145	151	157	163	169	174	180	186	192	197	204
65	114	120	126	132	138	144	150	156	162	168	174	180	186	192	198	204	210
66	118	124	130	136	142	148	155	161	167	173	179	186	192	198	204	210	216
67	121	127	134	140	146	153	159	166	172	178	185	191	198	204	211	217	223
68	125	131	138	144	151	158	164	171	177	184	190	197	203	210	216	223	230
69	128	135	142	149	155	162	169	176	182	189	196	203	209	216	223	230	236
70	132	139	146	153	160	167	174	181	188	195	202	209	216	222	229	236	243
71	136	143	150	157	165	172	179	186	193	200	208	215	222	229	236	243	250
72	140	147	154	162	169	177	184	191	199	206	213	221	228	235	242	250	258
73	144	151	159	166	174	182	189	197	204	212	219	227	235	242	250	257	265
74	148	155	163	171	179	186	194	202	210	218	225	233	241	249	256	264	272
75	152	160	168	176	184	192	200	208	216	224	232	240	248	256	264	272	279
76	156	164	172	180	189	197	205	213	221	230	238	246	254	263	271	279	287

Using this formula the World Health Organization (WHO) as well as the National Institutes of Health (NIH) classified a BMI of 18.5 to 25 as optimal, 25 to 30 as overweight, while a BMI greater than 30 would indicate obesity. The BMI ranges were based WHO data suggesting increasing health risks for people with BMI's above 25.

While BMI has been useful in research, especially when comparing large groups of people; it can be misleading for any one individual. For example, Arnold Schwarzeneggar, in his younger days as a body builder, had a BMI of 33, while Tom Cruise, another movie star, had a BMI of 31. Based on these numbers, both would be categorized as obese even though neither had excessive fat accumulations. **The simple explanation for these discrepancies is that muscle is heavier than fat tissue, so a muscular person will have an elevated BMI even if she has little fat on her body.**

Another problem with using BMI as an indicator of desirable weight is that the health risks associated with BMI are not the same for all ethnic groups. There's evidence that Asians have increased risks at lower BMI's, so a BMI of 23 to 27.5 would be overweight and 27.5 or higher would be obese for someone of Asian ancestry. Likewise there is some evidence that, for African-American females, the health risks increase at higher BMI's, so the usual cutoffs for overweight and obesity might not make sense for this population.[9]

Understanding the limitations of the BMI is helpful when working with clients who set their weight loss goals based on a BMI score. Chapter 11 presents methods for helping your client develop reasonable goals that aren't based on their BMI.

APPLES VS. PEARS

There are several other methods for determining obesity. Perhaps the most accurate, but least practical is hydrostatic weighing, or more simply, weighing under water. This procedure yields the body's density that then allows for a calculation of percent body fat. Measuring waist circumference is more practical and doesn't require any fancy equipment, just a simple tape measure. Waist circumference may not be the same as your belt size. Follow the directions on page 8 to measure waist circumference.

Compared to BMI, waist circumference may be a better measure of health risks because all fat is not created equal! Most of the negative health consequences attributed to obesity, including diabetes, cardiovascular disease, and some types of cancer are more accurately attributed to abdominal, fat.

HOW TO MEASURE WAIST CIRCUMFERENCE

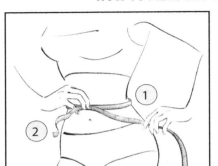

1. Position the tape mid-way between the top of your hip bone and the bottom of the rib cage

2. When taking measurment, the abdomen should be relaxed and you should be breathing out

Unlike fat in the buttocks, arms, and thighs, abdominal fat, particularly internal visceral fat, is associated with cardiovascular disease, type 2 diabetes and stroke.[10] While we tend to think of fat tissue as an inert blob just sitting inside our skin, this is not accurate. Belly fat is metabolically active, secreting a variety of hormones. This fat is wrapped around vital organs like the heart, lungs, and liver. It can contribute to inflammation and insulin resistance that can promote diabetes and the other illnesses that have been associated with obesity.[11]

The World Health Organization suggests that health risks increase when waist circumference reaches the following cut offs:

	MEN	WOMEN
Increased Risk	37″	31.5″
Substantially Increased Risk	40″	34.5″

People who tend to accumulate excess fat in their abdominal area can be described as having an apple shaped body while others who accumulate fat in their butts and thighs have a pear shaped body. As a rule, when men gain weight they tend to be apples while women are more often pears. People with pear fat have increased risk for varicose veins but that is much less dangerous than apple fat. While peripheral fat is more benign than visceral fat, it is more difficult to lose. If you're a typical pear shaped female, you may find it difficult to reduce the size of your butt and thighs while your husband has an easier time losing his belly fat.

One final point about apples and pears: the location of fat on the body is determined by genetics. You have some control over how much fat will be on your body. If you eat less and exercise more you'll probably lose fat, but you can't control where the weight loss will come from. Unfortunately some of your clients will judge the success of their weight loss efforts based on changes (or lack of changes) in the body part they find most troubling. A client could lose weight and improve her health risks but be dissatisfied because she thinks that her thighs are still too big. Understanding the genetic determinants of fat distribution will help prevent clients from getting discouraged and giving up on their behavior changes.

Like most men, I'm apple shaped. So when I joined a gym several years ago, I immediately started on abdominal exercises using the crunch machine. Over several months I did this exercise hoping that it would reduce the size of my midsection. While I was successful in increasing the amount of weight I could pull with my crunches, the exercise had no effect on my visceral fat; I just developed strong abdominal muscles around the visceral fat. This experience taught me that, regardless if it's a realistic exercise or some pie-in-the-sky miracle cream or belt, there's nothing that will work as a "spot reducer."

Understanding the genetic determinants of fat distribution and body shape can be helpful working with your clients. Chapter 9 discusses the role body shape plays in determining weight loss goals and how to help clients address these issues in order to develop more realistic goals.

HEALTH AT EVERY SIZE?

It's hard to ignore newspaper articles and media reports about "the obesity epidemic." We're bombarded with reports about the health risks and economic costs of obesity: $147 billion in 2008, according to one estimate. Recently there's been a movement arguing that the war on obesity is misguided. According to the Health At Every Size website, this view ". . . *is based on the simple premise that the best way to improve health is to honor your body. . . Health at Every Size encourages: Accepting and respecting the natural diversity of body sizes and shapes.*" The basic idea is that the focus on weight as a health risk is ill advised; you can be heavy and still be healthy. They suggest that the medical consequences attributed to obesity are not the result of obesity per se, but rather the effects of unhealthy yo-yo dieting. They encourage increasing physical activity not to lose weight but rather to improve health.

The view that you can be obese and healthy was supported by the 2013 publication of a study that was widely quoted in the popular media. *The*

New York Times even ran an Op-Ed piece about "Our Absurd Fear of Fat." The study was a meta-analysis (a method of combining data from several studies) of almost 3 million individuals and more than 270,000 deaths. It found that, compared to normal weight individuals, overweight (BMI 25-30) was ". . .associated with significantly lower all-cause mortality" while Grade 1 obesity (BMI 30-35) did not have a greater risk of mortality. Only with BMIs above 35 did the risk of death increase.[12] While this doesn't support the idea that you can be healthy at any weight, it does suggest that being overweight is beneficial and health risks don't increase until the BMI is above 35.

Given the obvious appeal of the counter-intuitive findings that obesity isn't a health risk and being overweight may even be protective, your clients might question the need to lose weight. This could put you in the difficult position of conveying the disappointing news that, despite being published in a highly respected journal, the conclusions are questionable. The methodology of the study has been criticized. For example, the effects of smoking or being ill were not adequately controlled and the study didn't account for the relationship between age and weight gain or loss. Also, modern medicine has increased lifespan but living longer with a chronic obesity-related disease might not be a desirable outcome. *Quality vs. Longevity*

Other studies have supported the view that obesity is unhealthy. For example, an earlier meta-analysis of 1.46 million white men and women between the ages of 19 – 84 found obese individuals to be two and a half times as likely to die young.[13] Canadian researchers compared mortality data for normal weight people who were metabolically healthy with metabolically healthy obese individuals in a meta-analysis involving 60,000 adults followed-up for 10 years or more. They concluded that there is no healthy pattern of obesity.[14] Another study examined weight and age concluding, "young adults who are obese have more than a 50% lifetime risk of diabetes and cardiovascular disease, and those with severe obesity might expect to spend a third of their remaining life with a major chronic disorder."[15] These findings are important because they show that the effect of obesity on the number of healthy years lost is greater than it's effect on life expectancy. In other words, even if obesity doesn't shorten the lifespan, it increases the likelihood of a chronic illness.

One of the goals of the Health At Every Size movement is to remove the stigma attached to obesity. While this is a worthwhile goal, and lessening the stigma should make weight loss easier, the bulk of the evidence doesn't support the idea that you can be healthy and significantly obese.

ENDNOTES

1. Puhl, R. M. & Heuer, C. A. (2009). The stigma of obesity: A review and update. *Obesity, 17,* 941–964.

2. Sitton, S. & Blanchard, S. (1995). Men's preferences in romantic partners: obesity vs. addiction. *Psychological Reports, 77,* 1185–1186.

3. Puhl, R. M. & Brownell, K. D. (2006). Confronting and coping with weight stigma: an investigation of overweight and obese adults. *Obesity, 14,* 1802–1815.

4. Puhl, R. M., Gold, J. A., Luedicke, J. & DePierre, J. A. (2013). The effect of physicians' body weight on patient attitudes: Implication for physician selection, trust, and adherence to medical advice. *International Journal of Obesity* doi: 10. 1038/ijo.2013.33

5. Maroney, D., & Golub, S. (1992). Nurses' attitudes toward obese persons and certain ethnic groups. *Perceptual and Motor Skills, 75,* 387–391.

6. Friedman, R. R. & Puhl, R. M. (2012). Weight Bias: A social Justice issue. A policy brief. New Haven: Yale Rudd Center for Food Policy & Obesity.

7. Yalom, I. D. (1989). *Love's executioner & other tales of psychotherapy.* New York: Harper Perennial, p. 87–88.

8. Lillis, J., Luoma, J. B., Levin, M. E. & Hayes, S. C. (2010). Measuring weight self-stigma: The weight self-stigma questionnaire. *Obesity, 18,* 971–976.

9. Carroll, J. F., Chiapa, A. L., Rodriquez, M., Phelps, D. R., Cardarelli, K. M., Vishwanatha, J. K., Bae, S. and Cardarelli, R. (2008), Visceral Fat, Waist Circumference, and BMI: Impact of Race/ethnicity. *Obesity, 16*: 600–607.

10. Bjornstorp, P. (2002). Definition and classification of obesity. In C. G Fairburn & K. D. Brownell (Eds.), *Eating disorders and obesity: A comprehensive handbook (2nd ed.)* (pp. 377-381), New York: Guilford.

11. Lustig, R. H. (2013). *Fat Chance: Beating the odds against sugar, processed food, obesity, and disease.* New York: Hudson Street Press.

12. Flegal, K. M., Kit, B. K., Orpana, H. & Graubard, B. I. (2013). Association of all-cause mortality with overweight and obesity using standard body mass index categories: A systematic review and meta-analysis. *Journal of the American Medical Association, 309,* 71–82.

13. Berrington de Gonzales, A., Hartge, P., Cerhan, J. R., et al. (2010). Body-mass index and mortality among 1.46 million white adults. *New England Journal of Medicine, 363,* 2211–2219.

14. Kramer, C.K., Zinman, B., Retnakaran, R. (2013). Are metabolically healthy overweight and obesity benign conditions?: A systematic review and meta-analysis. *Annals of Internal Medicine. 159,* 758–769.

15. Grover, S.A. Kaouache, M., Rempel, P., et al. (2014). Years of life lost and healthy life-years lost from diabetes and cardiovascular disease in overweight and obese people: a modeling study. *Lancet Diabetes Endocrinology.* (published online Dec 5.) http://dx.doi.org/10.1016/S2213-8587(14)70229-3.

CHAPTER 2

Why Gaining Is Easy But Losing Is Hard

If you live in the U.S. it's quite likely that if you just go about your normal business you'll gain weight. It won't be because you have any of the shameful personal characteristics described in Chapter 1, but rather because you live in an environment that makes it easy to gain weight and hard to lose it. In this chapter, we'll examine many of the variables that make it so easy to gain, and distinguish between those that you can control vs. the others that you can't.

Clients typically are confused or may hold erroneous beliefs about the source of their weight difficulties. They may attribute their weight gain to anything ranging from the Freshman 15 (a myth)[16] to food allergies, or an unhappy childhood. By helping clients understand how weight is determined, they'll likely be relieved to discover that it's not just a matter of "will power" or a vague medical or psychological condition, but rather a complex interaction of many genetic, physiological, and environmental variables. Knowing which of the variables are under your client's control and which aren't will help reduce self-stigmatization. With less guilt and recrimination, his motivation to make the behavioral changes needed for weight control will increase. He'll be more able to establish realistic weight goals, and make permanent lifestyle changes that will avoid the disappointment that comes with repeated dieting failures.

IS THE FAT IN YOUR GENES?

Unfortunately, regardless of their efforts, clients cannot control one of the most powerful determinants of weight; it's in their genes. In a now classic study,[17] Dr. Claude Bouchard and colleagues overfed 12 pairs of male twins. For 12 weeks, in a controlled environment, they consumed 1,000 more calories than they needed each day. Although each twin gained about the same amount as his brother, the amount of weight the different twin pairs gained varied. With the same overfeeding some of the subjects gained 9.5 lbs. while others gained as much as 29.3 lbs. The discouraging truth is that some people inherit a tendency to gain weight easily.

The thrifty gene hypothesis[18] is one possible explanation for the heritability of weight. Basically, our prehistoric ancestors had to cope with a variable food supply. When there was a famine due to drought, a harsh winter, or war with a neighboring tribe, many people, especially children, died. The folks who were more efficient at storing energy (fat is stored energy) during times of plenty were more likely to survive during the lean years and then reproduce. Their children inherited the ability to efficiently store energy, so after numerous generations many of us easily gain weight when food is available even though it's unlikely that we'll experience famine.

Most of your clients live near a supermarket stocked with calorically dense foods that are easily affordable, and there's a McDonald's or other fast food dispensary within driving distance. We live in an environment sometimes referred to as "obesegenetic": our environment helps us get fat because it's just not suited to our genetic makeup.

David Katz, MD, Director of the Yale Prevention Research Center, draws an illustrative analogy: Over many thousands of years polar bears have evolved overlapping mechanisms to conserve heat so that they can survive in their harsh, frigid environment. They soak up and retain heat but if you put them in the desert, where it's hot, they would continue to soak up heat, get overheated and have difficulty surviving. They are ill suited to live in the desert. Similarly, humans evolved in an environment where food was scarce and there was a constant need to soak up and retain energy. But in our current environment, where food is plentiful, we get fat.

Although there is clear evidence that genes help to determine weight, it isn't as simple as identifying THE obesity gene. A recent review suggests that there are hundreds of genes that contribute to determining an individual's weight.[19] It's possible that there's one or more genes that determine basal metabolism, another set of genes that determine the length of time it takes to get hungry, different genes that control how much food is needed to feel full, and so on. Given that so many genes are involved in weight regulation it's unlikely that in the foreseeable future there will be any way of modifying our genetic makeup to lessen the likelihood of obesity.

While genes clearly influence weight, recent research suggests that the environment can influence the expression of the gene. Researchers have found that a variant of the FTO gene is associated with obesity. One copy of the gene results in an average of an extra 3.5 pounds, while two copies increase the risk of obesity by 50 percent. A recent study[20] reviewed FTO data collected over 60 years and found that people born before the 1940s with the risky gene were less likely to be obese compared with people with the same gene but born more recently. These findings suggest that environmental influences, perhaps the modern diet and all the labor saving devices that reduce the need to be physically active, have altered the expression of the FTO gene. In other words, the environment can impact the effect of one of the genes contributing to obesity. While this research needs to be replicated, and only deals with one of many genes involved with obesity, it has profound implications that are important for your clients.

If your client has family members who are obese, they may have inherited a tendency to easily gain weight, but their destiny is not fixed. They won't be able to change their genetics, but by making behavioral changes they may be able to reduce the effect of the genes contributing to obesity.

NATURE VS. NURTURE

Although we know that genetics can play an important role in determining weight, there's no way of knowing how much of an individual's weight is inherited versus a result of his behavior. To examine the role of heritability in determining weight, there have been many studies comparing the similarity of the weights of twins (identical vs. fraternal twins), or the weight of adopted children compared with their adoptive vs. biological parents, or similarity of weights within families. The studies yield greatly variable results suggesting that anywhere between 30 to 70 percent of BMI is determined by genetics.[21] Even if we knew what percent of weight was determined by heredity the resulting figure would be an estimate for the whole population. We still wouldn't know the genetic component of any individual's weight.

Your client might assume that she is programmed to get fat because everyone in her family is obese but family members typically have similar environments and developmental histories so genetics might not be the primary determinant of her obesity. Furthermore, it probably wouldn't be helpful for your client to know his genetic predisposition to be fat or thin. If he knew that he was genetically predisposed to gain weight he might get discouraged and give up on any attempt to control his eating ("What's the use; I'm going to be fat anyway. I might as well...") and as a result he would gain more weight.

What would be helpful for your client is knowing where she is genetically predisposed to accumulate fat tissue. Recall from the discussion of apples and pears in Chapter 1 that the location of fat on the body is determined by genetics. While there's no genetic test, your client can make a good guess by looking at her parents and siblings to see which part of their bodies tend to collect fat. Often successful weight loss still leaves the client feeling dissatisfied because she still doesn't have her ideal shape. Understanding the genetic basis of fat distribution will help avoid discouragement when her weight control efforts don't result in a "perfect" figure.

ENVIRONMENT AND CHOICE MATTER: NOT ALL OF THE FAT IS IN YOUR GENES

Although we may have evolved to efficiently store energy, our genetic predisposition isn't sufficient to explain the current obesity epidemic. As recently as 1980 about 20 percent of us were overweight while now the number is closer to 33 percent and the number of morbidly obese (100 lbs. or more overweight) has quadrupled. In the same time period the rate of juvenile obesity has tripled.[22] Clearly evolution doesn't take place over 20 or 30 years. Our genetic makeup hasn't changed in this time period so we need to consider something else: the effects of the environment on weight.

It's important for clients to know that eating habits and the environment have a lot to do with weight. This brings in the idea of choice and change, which is empowering. Cross-cultural comparisons demonstrate the effects of the environment on weight. For example, the Pima Indians of Arizona have tremendous problems with obesity and the highest prevalence of type 2 diabetes of all Americans. If you compare them with their genetically similar Pima cousins in the Sierra Madre Mountains of Mexico, you'll find that obesity was 10 times more frequent in the American Pima men and three times as likely in American Pima women.[23] It's likely that the shift from the traditional agriculturally based diet to a typical American diet with a greater proportion of processed foods is responsible for the greater prevalence of obesity and diabetes in the Arizona Pimas.

Another example of the effects of culture and environment can be found in Qatar, the tiny, oil-rich sheikdom on the Arabian Peninsula. Qataris have the highest per capita income and, according to some estimates, the Qataris-not Americans-are the fattest humans on the planet. Seventy-three percent of Qatari men and 70 percent of Qatari women are obese or overweight, but it wasn't always so. In two generations, the Qataris went from a traditional tribal lifestyle to living in air-conditioned villas, loving fast food, and delegating any physical labor to servants.[24] Regardless if it's Arizona, the Middle East or anywhere else in the world, when a culture transitions from a traditional lifestyle to an American pattern of eating and activity, weight gain follows despite genetics.

Perphaps the most dramatic example of the effects of the environment on weight, an example that should resonate with your clients, is the increase in the sugar content of the foods we eat. Sugar consumption has doubled in the last 30 years.[25] Americans consume an average of 6.5 ounces per day, or about 130 pounds of sugar each year. Sugar now comprises between 20 to 25 percent of daily caloric consumption.[26] You can encourage your clients to examine the ingredient list on the packaged foods they buy to become aware of their sugar consumption. For many clients, the simplest way of reducing sugar intake is to avoid soda and other sugary beverages.

Dr. George Bray, one of the most influential obesity researchers, nicely summarized the research on genetics and the environment. He said, "Genes load the gun; the environment pulls the trigger." While there's not much your clients can do to alter the gun, Chapters 4 - 8 will offer methods you can use to help them to avoid pulling the trigger.

IS YOUR CLIENT A FOOD ADDICT?

The notion that obesity is a result of addiction to carbohydrate-laden, high fat foods has been popular for many years. Traditionally food addiction has been conceptualized using a 12-step model similar to Alcoholics Anonymous.[27] Although it remains controversial, recent research with animals and humans has lent support to the idea that food can be addicting.[28] Proponents of this view include Nora Volkow, MD, Director of the National Institute on Drug Abuse. She said,

> *The data is so overwhelming the field has to accept it. We are finding tremendous overlap between drugs in the brain and food in the brain.*[29]

Other scientists disagree, pointing out that the biological consequences of food don't make it an addictive substance.[30] Activities such as sex and sleep also have biological consequences but that doesn't make them physiologically addicting.

In discussing food addiction, it's necessary to distinguish between true physiological addiction in which the substance affects brain function (e.g., addiction to alcohol or opiates) and a process addiction that doesn't involve taking brain-affecting substances. Compulsive shopping or computer game playing would be examples of process addictions.

Proponents of food as an addictive substance point to studies of brain function to support the view that it is a true physiological addiction, not a process addiction. Opponents point to behavioral differences. For example, a heroin addict deprived of his drug for eight hours would readily use the drug if given the opportunity. In contrast, many self-identified food addicts claim they're not hungry and refuse to eat breakfast despite not having had anything to eat for eight hours while they slept.

While the scientific validity of the concept of food addiction is still unsettled, some of your clients will self-identify as "chocoholics", "food addicts" or use similar terminology to explain their eating difficulties. They might make reference to self-scoring questionnaires offered by 12-step programs (e.g., Food Addicts in Recovery Anonymous) as evidence of their addiction. These questionnaires have not been scientifically validated and with overly inclusive questions (e.g., "Do you eat when you're not hungry?"), the questionnaire is likely to yield false positives.

The 12-step programs advocate abstinence. Since you can't completely abstain from eating, defining abstinence for eating problems is more problematic than defining abstinence from alcohol or drugs. For example, Food Addicts in Recovery Anonymous defines abstinence as "weighed and measured meals with nothing in between, no flour, no sugar and the avoidance of any individual binge foods". This approach, which eliminates specific foods or food groups, is consistent with rigid dieting. Some of the pitfalls of dieting are discussed in Chapter 3.

If your client reports that she is a food addict, instead of directly challenging your client's self-identification, you can use the information presented in Chapter 3 to discourage rigid dieting while not challenging her belief that she's addicted to sugar, carbs, chocolate or any a specific food or food group. For example, Robert Lustig, M.D. notes that sugar is found in most processed foods. If your client reports that she's addicted to sugar, you could suggest that it's unlikely that she could completely eliminate it from her diet. Instead you could encourage her to reduce sugar consumption and follow Dr. Lustig's suggestion to increase fiber in her diet to mitigate the effects of sugar.[31]

HELP MAY BE ON THE WAY

Chapter 3 will include a review of the current medical and surgical methods for weight loss, but new research may yield novel methods in the near future. While it's unlikely that anything will modify the genetic basis of obesity, it may be possible to alter how food is processed inside the body. Even when you're all by yourself you're not alone. It's been estimated that the human gut is home to about 100 trillion microorganisms. All together they probably weigh as much as the human brain. These little bugs play a role in extracting energy during the digestion of food. A recent study showed that gut bacteria could contribute to obesity. Researchers found pairs of human twins where one was obese and the other wasn't. They transferred gut bacteria from the humans to mice. The mice receiving bacteria from the fat human twins got fat, mice getting bacteria from thin twins didn't.[32] If researchers can isolate the types of microorganism that alter digestion so that fewer calories were absorbed, it might be possible to develop supplements containing "good" bacteria that would promote weight loss. Despite the future possibility of helpful bacteria, there aren't any probiotics currently available that can reliably produce weight loss.

While our genetics combined with an obesigenic environment make it easy to gain weight and hard to lose it, all is not lost. Your clients cannot modify their genetic codes nor change their surrounding culture. With your help, your clients can learn to modify their individual environment to reduce the cues that promote unnecessary eating and alter the expression of genes that would produce weight gain.

ENDNOTES

16. Zagorsky, J. L. & Smith, P. K. (2011). The Freshman 15: A critical time for obesity intervention or media myth? *Social Science Quarterly, 92,* 1389–1407.

17. Bouchard, C., Tremblay, A., Despres, J. P., Nadequ, A., Lupien, P. J., Theriault, G., Dussault, J., Moorjani, S., Pinault, S., & Fournier, G. (1990). The response to long-term overfeeding in identical twins. *New England Journal of Medicine, 24,* 1477–1482.

18. Prentice, A. M. (2005). Early influences on human energy regulation: Thrifty genotypes and thrifty phenotypes. *Physiology and Behavior, 86,* 640–645.

19. Rankinen, T., Zuberi, A., Chagnon, Y. C., Weisnagel, S. J., Argyropoulos, G., Walts, B., Pérusse, L. & Bouchard, C. (2006). The Human Obesity Gene Map: The 2005 Update, *Obesity, 14,* 529–644.

20. Rosenquist, J. N., Lehrer, S. F., O'Malley, A. J., Zaslavsky, A. M., Smoller, J. W. & Christakis, N. A. (2014). Cohort of birth modifies the association between FTO genotype and BMI. *PNAS, 112,* 354–359.

21. Bouchard, C. (2002). Genetic influences on body weight. In. C. G. Fairburn & K. D. Brownell (Eds.), *Eating disorders and obesity: A comprehensive handbook (2nd ed.)* (pp. 16-21), New York: Guilford.

22. King, B. M. (2013). The modern obesity epidemic, ancestral hunter-gatherers, and the sensory/reward control of food intake. *American Psychologist, 68,* 88–96.

23. Schulz, L. O., Bennett, P. H., Ravussin, E., Kidd, J. R., Kidd, K. K., Esparza, J., & Valencia, M. E. (2006). Effects of traditional and western environments on prevalence of type 2 diabetes in Pima Indians in Mexico and the U. S. *Diabetes Care, 29,* 1866–1871.

24. Edwards, H. S. (2011, November 16). The richest, fattest nation on earth (It's not the United States). *The Atlantic http://www.theatlantic.com/health/archive/2011/11/the-richest-fattest-nation-on-earth-its-not-the-united-states/248366/*

25. Vos, M. B. et al. (2008). Dietary fructose consumption among US children and adults: The Third National Health and Nutrition Examination Survey. *Medscape Journal of Medicine, 10,* 160.

26. Johnson, R. K. et al. (2009). Dietary sugars intake and cardiovascular health: A scientific statement from the American Heart Association, *Circulation, 120,* 1011–1020.

27. Overeaters Anonymous (1998). *The twelve steps and twelve traditions of Overeaters Anonymous.* Rio Rancho, NM: Overeaters Anonymous.

28. Volkow, N. D., Wang, G-J., Tomasi, D., & Baler, R. D. (2013). The addictive dimensionality of obesity. *Biological Psychiatry, 73,* 811–818.

29. Quoted in: Langreth, R. & Stanford, D. D. (2011, Nov. 6). Science zeros in on food as a drug. *Herald Tribune,* p. A1.

30. Ziauddeen, H. & Fletcher, P. C. (2012). Is food addiction a valid and useful concept? *Obesity Reviews, 14,* 19–28.
    Benton, D. (2010). The plausibility of sugar addiction and its role in obesity and eating disorders. *Clinical Nutrition, 29,* 288–303.

31. Lustig, R. H. (2013). *Fat chance: Beating the odds against sugar, processed food, obesity, and disease.* New York: Hudson Street Press.

32. Ridaura, V. K., Faith, J. J., Rey, F. E., Cheng, J., Duncan, A. E., Kau, A. L., Lombard, V., Henrissat, B., Bain, J. R., Muehlbauer, M. J., Ilkayeva, O., Ursell, L. K., Clemente, J. C., Van Treuren, W., Walters, W. A., Newgard, C. B., Knight, R., Heath, A. C., and Gordon, J. I. (2013). Gut microbiota from twins discordant for obesity modulate metabolism in mice. *Science 341:* 1241214 doi: 10.1126/science.1241214

Chapter 3

Diets, Drugs, Supplements and Surgery: What Works?

According to one estimate, 55 percent of women and 29 percent of men have been dieting in the past year. If any of your clients are heavy or just weight conscious they're probably included in these statistics. Unfortunately, they probably weren't successful in losing or if they did lose, they probably were unable to maintain their weight loss. Your clients' discouraging experience is consistent with the oft-cited gloomy conclusion, "Most obese persons will not stay in treatment, most will not lose weight, and of those who do lose weight, most will regain it." Although following a typical diet is a flawed strategy, the 95 percent failure statistic is unrealistically pessimistic. It comes from a 1950's study in which 100 participants were just given a printed diet and sent on their way.[33]

Even more recent studies may not provide an accurate picture of weight loss outcomes since most studies were conducted with participants in weight loss programs. This may contribute to a negative bias because many people who lost weight on their own, without participating in a formal program, would not have been included in the outcome data. Although weight loss is still a challenge, the currently available methods are far superior to just offering a printed diet; your overweight clients shouldn't abandon all efforts.

GETTING OFF THE DIET ROLLER COASTER

One client told me, "I've lost 100 pounds, but it was the same 10 pounds ten times."

Yo-Yo dieting occurs when a diet results in weight loss that is followed by weight gain, often with a few additional pounds, followed by a period of discouragement, followed by yet another diet. Like many of her peers, your dieting client may be discouraged but still holds out hope that the new diet she saw on the best-seller list or touted on a TV program will finally be the diet that actually works. You can help your client stop yo-yoing by providing accurate information about caloric restriction and offering practical, non-dieting suggestions for weight loss.

A good place to start is to measure your client's dietary restraint (attempts to restrict food intake to lose weight). The Revised Restraint Scale has been used in dozens of studies that have yielded important findings about the effects of habitual dieting.

THE REVISED RESTRAINT SCALE

For each item, circle the response that best describes your experience.

(1) How often are you dieting?

Never   Rarely   Sometimes   Usually   Always

(2) What is the maximum amount of weight (in pounds) you have ever lost within one month?

0-4   5-9   10-14   15-19   20+

(3) What is your maximum weight gain within a week?

0-1   1.1-2   2.1-3   3.1-5   5.1+

(4) In a typical week, how much does your weight fluctuate?

0-1   1.1-2   2.1-3   3.1-5   5.1+

(5) Would a weight fluctuation of five pounds affect the way you live your life?

Not at all   Slightly   Moderately   Extremely

(6) Do you eat sensibly in front of others and splurge alone?

Never   Rarely   Often   Always

(7) Do you give too much time and thought to food?

Never   Rarely   Often   Always

(8) Do you have feelings of guilt after overeating?

Never   Rarely   Often   Always

(9) How conscious are you of what you're eating?

Not at all   Slightly   Moderately   Extremely

(10) How many pounds over your desired weight were you at your maximum weight?

0-1   1-5   6-10   11-20   21+

To score the scale, give each response in the first column on the left (e.g., Never, Not at all) a 0, each response in the second column (e.g., Rarely, Slightly) a 1, each response in the third column (e.g., Sometimes, Often) a 2, and so on. Then add the numbers to get the Restraint Score. For women a score of 16 or above is considered indicative of dietary restraint, while for men 12 or higher indicates restrained eating.

Many studies have demonstrated that high restraint scores are associated with weight loss failure. In a classic study, psychologists Herman and Mack gave subjects a milkshake (the "preload") and then offered them ice cream. After consuming the milkshake, the restrained eaters ate more ice cream than the unrestrained eaters who'd had the same milkshakes.[34] Along with other studies, these findings suggest that when dietary restraint is broken subsequent eating increases. Thus, having a milkshake, which isn't on the diet, caused the restrained eaters to give up control and eat more ice cream. Other studies have demonstrated an emotional upset, drinking alcoholic beverages or anything else that would upset a rigid diet is likely to result in increased eating or may precipitate binge eating. It's also likely that with a history of restraint the habitual dieter has learned to override the signals of hunger and satiety that normally regulate eating. As a result, once the diet is abandoned, he doesn't have guidelines to help control eating.

If chronic dieting is counter productive should you encourage your clients to just give up and accept the health and psychological consequences of being overweight? Despite the failure of most diets, there are changes your clients can make that will promote a healthy weight.

UNDERSTANDING FOOD CHOICE AND WEIGHT

Your client is probably confused - low carb vs. low fat, eat like a caveman (Paleo) or eat like an Italian (Mediterranean), avoid gluten, avoid sugar, or go vegan? Despite all the hype and the never-ending controversy, in terms of weight loss, it probably doesn't matter. A Kansas State University professor lost 27 pounds in just 10 weeks eating junk (Oreos, Doritos, Twinkies, etc.) but limiting his consumption to 1,800 calories per day, although he did "cheat" by having a protein shake, a can of green beans and four celery stalks each day.[35] Although it didn't include junk food diets, a recent meta-analysis combing the results from 59 different studies found that, "Weight loss differences between individual named diets were small."[36]

Ask your client, "Have you ever had a meal, felt full so you refused seconds of the main course, but then found room in your stomach when the hostess brought out the dessert?" This is an example of sensory specific satiety. As you eat more of a food the appeal of that food declines, but your appetite is revived when there's a new food. This is the "secret ingredient" in virtually all diets; they limit food choices so you eat less. Studies with both animals and humans show that there's more eating and increased weight when there's more variety in the diet and less eating when there are fewer choices.[37]

To gain weight, eat at an all-you-can eat buffet with dozens of choices available. To lose weight limit your consumption to cabbage soup or grapefruit or rice or any of the other fad diet foods. Even more reasonable diets will restrict food choices. For example, if your client is on a low fat diet he won't have bacon or burgers while if he's on a low carb diet he can't have pasta and pizza; most diets will forbid some foods. This approach works for as long as he can maintain the restraint but invariably the appeal and cravings for the forbidden foods will increase until there's an emotional upset, a little too much alcohol, or anything else breaking the restraint causing the diet to be abandoned. After consuming or perhaps bingeing on the forbidden foods the failed dieter will have feelings of guilt and self-recrimination.

Unfortunately all the attention devoted to dieting controversies obscures what may be a more significant contributor to the obesity epidemic: portion size. Numerous studies have demonstrated that average portion sizes have increased in both restaurant meals ("Supersize it?") and meals made at home. Not so long ago bagels were two ounces with 160 calories but now they're likely to weigh as much as 10 ounces and supply 800 calories not including cream cheese or anything else. One study found that between 1977 and 1994-1996 increases in portion size accounted for an additional 93 calories for snacks, 49 calories for soft drinks, 97 calories for hamburgers and 133 calories for Mexican dishes.[38] The USDA estimated that in 2010 consumption averaged 2,534 calories per person per day, an increase of 448 calories per day compared with 1970 consumption. Whether it's at a restaurant or a meal at home, people have just become accustomed to eating more than they need.

Eating too much is easy to do because regardless of age, educational level, body weight or gender most people don't correctly assess the amount that they're eating.[39] Judging the appropriate serving size isn't easy since clients don't usually have measuring cups or scales to measure the portion they're taking. The following chart should help.

Portion Size Guide	
1 cup	baseball
1/2 cup	lightbulb
1 oz or 2 tbsp	golf ball
1 tbsp	poker chip
3 oz chicken or meat	deck of cards
3 oz fish	checkbook
1 oz lunch meat	compact disk
3 oz muffin or biscuit	hockey puck
1 1/2 oz cheese	3 dice
1 slice of bread	cassette tape

MEAL REPLACEMENTS

There are many options in the marketplace for weight loss, from meal replacements to social-supported diet programs. It can be helpful to be familiar with these options, many of which will be known to your clients. One strategy to reduce caloric intake and portion size is to use prepackaged meals and meal replacements that are shipped directly to customer. The companies (e.g., HMR, Medifast) vary in the frequency and amount of outside foods allowed. For example, HMR provides all the food except for four one-cup servings of fruit and vegetables while Medifast provides the food for four meals each day supplemented by one meal of five ounces of lean protein and three servings of non-starchy vegetables.

One study, funded by Medifast[40] compared Medifast with dieters given advice on how to meet a 1,000-calorie per day goal. While there were dropouts in both groups, people in the Medifast group lost 16.5 pounds after six months while regular dieters lost 8.4 pounds. At the end of a year members of both groups had regained weight but the Medifast group was still superior, maintaining a ten pound loss vs. four pounds for the control group.

SlimFast shake mixes and snack bars are widely available in grocery stores and on-line. They are intended to replace breakfast, lunch and snacks when, combined with a 500-calorie dinner, total 1,200 calories daily. A German study[41] compared a 1,200-calorie diet with SlimFast liquid meal replacements for two of the three daily meals. After three months the diet group lost 3.3 pounds while the SlimFast group lost 17 pounds. The participants were then told to use the SlimFast to replace one meal. After four years participants maintained an average 18.5-pound weight loss.

DIET-BASED PROGRAMS

Many of your overweight clients will have tried, or be curious about commercial weight loss programs. Perhaps you've been asked what you think about Weight Watchers vs. Jenny Craig or Nutrisystem. In addition to the widely advertised commercial programs there are on-line programs, self-help organizations, and medical modified fasts.

The commercial programs such as Weight Watchers and Jenny Craig typically advocate diets that are neither low carb nor low fat. The programs differ in how the recommended diet is delivered and the type of social support provided. Thus Weight Watchers doesn't forbid any food but uses a point system to provide choice while restricting caloric intake. The point values favor foods that are nutritionally dense thereby promoting satiety. In contrast, Jenny Craig and Nutrisystem provide calorie controlled packaged foods. Jenny Craig participants eat the packaged meals until they're halfway to their weight loss goals then prepare their own meals twice a week until they reach their goal when they transition to all home prepared meals. Nutrisystem is similar although they claim that a five-pound weight loss is possible in the first week, followed by one to two pound weekly weight losses.

Traditionally Weight Watchers participants attend weekly group meetings in which there is a private weigh-in and discussion conducted by a non-professional group leader. Recently they've added phone and on-line coaching in lieu of the group meetings. Jenny Craig also has a weekly weigh-in but instead of group meetings there are individual sessions with a non-professional counselor. In contrast, Nutrisystem has neither group nor individual sessions although online or phone consultations are available.

US News & World Report rated weight loss diets and programs and concluded that:

> *Weight Watchers bested all other ranked diets for both short-term and long-term weight loss. That doesn't guarantee it will work for everyone, of course. Its average rating of "moderately effective" for long-term weight loss reflects the difficulty dieters have in staying on the wagon, even when using the best weight-loss diet available.*

Their conclusions were based on several studies that have demonstrated significant weight loss with Weight Watchers. For example one 48-week study found an average weight loss of 13.2 pounds.[42] Another study comparing Weight Watchers with Jenny Craig and three medications (Qsymia, Belviq, and Orlistat) found that Weight Watchers was the most cost effective with an average expense of $70.50 per pound lost.[43]

NON-PROFIT GROUP METHODS

One problem with commercial programs is the expense can be prohibitive. Two widely available non-profit programs are Take off Pounds Sensibly (TOPS) and Overeaters Anonymous. Unlike Weight Watchers, volunteers who are elected by the chapter members, lead the TOPS meetings. A recent study[44] found that TOPS members who remained in the program for at least one year lost about six percent of their initial weight. The researchers noted the average loss was comparable to the results of Weight Watchers.

Overeaters Anonymous (OA) is a 12-Step program similar to Alcoholics Anonymous that is open to anyone with eating issues including people with bulimia nervosa, anorexia nervosa, and binge eating disorder. There's no specified diet and no religious beliefs are propounded although the program does include a spiritual component. The program advocates abstinence from compulsive eating but does not provide a definition of abstinence other than avoiding individual trigger foods and behaviors. An OA survey reported on their website[45] claims that 69 percent of their members have lost an average of 45 pounds and 51 percent are maintaining a "healthy weight." An independently conducted survey[46] found that participants who had been in the program for an average of 5.7 years lost an average of 21.8 pounds. While many weight conscious individuals would have difficulty subscribing to the OA ideology (e.g., ". . .a Power greater than ourselves could restore us to sanity"), there is evidence that the program does benefit a subset of primarily white overweight females.

WEB-BASED METHODS

While the web offers endless posts on diet and weight, much of it inaccurate, the most promising applications make use of smartphones or wearable activity and diet trackers. One of the most widely used applications is www.myfitnesspal.com. It includes an extensive listing of the caloric value of over four million foods including brand names and restaurant selections so that your client can self-monitor food intake. Instead of writing down everything she can use her smartphone to check the foods consumed and the app tallies the total number of calories. Over time it "learns" the typical foods that the user eats so there's less need to scroll through long lists of foods when making an entry. The app also allows detailed tracking of physical activity and calculates the caloric expenditure based on the user's weight. For example, an hour of sitting in a boat fishing burns 170 calories for a 150-pound person versus 238 calories used when fishing while standing on the shore. Users can also share their progress on Facebook and other social media websites.

Studies of the effects of web-based methods are inconclusive. A recent study of MyFitnessPal used in a primary care medical setting found no difference in weight loss after six months compared with a control group.[47] The researchers noted that logins to MyFitnessPal decreased sharply after the first month suggesting that it's only useful if people are willing to self-monitor. In contrast, a study of participants in a VA outpatient clinic found that adding mobile technology to biweekly group meetings resulted in an additional 8.5 pounds lost after six months.[48] A meta-analysis of web-based programs found statistically significant but minimal additional weight loss compared with a control group.[49] The authors concluded that the effect of internet programs was inconsistent depending on the type of usage or the period of use.

There are several wearable devices that will transmit activity data to a smartphone app that will generate charts and graphs. For example, a Fitbit that is worn on the wrist will monitor steps, distance walked, stairs climbed, calories burned, and sleep patterns. The Apple Watch also provides feedback including how often you stood-up to take a break from sitting and delivers reminders and suggests personal fitness goals. These devices measure caloric expenditure only, but the data collected can be downloaded into one of the web applications.

SUPPLEMENTS

If your client watches Dr. Oz on TV she may have heard him claim:

> *"You may think magic is make believe but this little bean has scientists saying they've found the magic weight loss cure for every body type—it's green coffee extract."*

or

> *"I've got the No. 1 miracle in a bottle to burn your fat. It's raspberry ketones."*

or

> *"Garcinia Cambogia. It may be the simple solution you've been looking for to bust your body fat for good."*

Despite Dr. Oz's very impressive medical credentials and the huge audience for his program, these exaggerated claims have no basis in fact. Green coffee, raspberry ketones and any of the dozens of other supplements sold for weight loss either have not been subjected to controlled outcome studies or, when they have been studied produce little or no more weight loss than placebos. For example, garcinia cambogia, a supplement derived from the rind of a fruit found in India is claimed to burn fat. A meta-analysis of clinical trials found no evidence for weight loss.[50] If your client is determined to try an unregulated supplement you can point out that, despite Dr. Oz's endorsement, the Federal Trade Commission banned deceptive advertising by marketers of green coffee bean supplements. You can help your client make realistic decisions about using supplements and avoid the disappointment when the anticipated weight loss isn't accomplished.

MEDICATION

If your client is a frustrated dieter, she may be considering weight-loss medication or possibly surgery. It would be helpful to know the options that are currently available. While the client should make the decision in consultation with his physician, you can help in the decision process by providing accurate information.

In 2012 the FDA approved Belviq (lorcaserin), the first new weight loss drug in 13 years. In prior years fen-phen was withdrawn after reports of fatal heart-valve problems, Meridia (sibutramine) was withdrawn after being linked to heart problems and Acomplia (rimonabant), which was never approved in the U.S., was withdrawn in Europe. The only weight loss drugs that were available were Xenical (orlistat), Alli, a lower dose of orlistat available without a prescription, and phentermine, a controlled substance that was approved only for short-term use.

Both orlistat and phentermine are still available but have significant disadvantages. Orlistat reduces caloric intake by inhibiting an enzyme necessary for digesting fat so that the fat passes through the digestive system and is eliminated. Although it results in modest weight loss (4.4-6.6 pounds after one year), the possible side effects include flatulence, "oily spotting" and fecal urgency. One of my clients jokingly asked, "Is it true that if you take Xenical you should wear brown pants?"

Phentermine, the benign component of fen-phen, is FDA approved for short-term (three months) use because of possible risks including elevation in blood pressure, tachycardia, insomnia, and addiction. It works as an appetite suppressant but is a controlled substance because of its potential for abuse. Since phentermine is off patent and inexpensive (less than $20 per month), none of the pharmaceutical companies have sponsored carefully controlled long-term studies. A recent study found no evidence of abuse or addiction in 269 clinic patients who had been taking the drug for up to 21 years.[51] Perhaps the three-month limitation is overly cautious. Many physicians have been prescribing the drug long term, ignoring the FDA guidelines.

Given the fatalities associated with fen-phen, the FDA was cautious in approving new drugs. Belviq, which is generally well tolerated, is a serotonin receptor agonist (probably not the best choice for a client on an SSRI) resulting in an average weight loss of 12.75 pounds over one year. Later in 2012, the FDA approved Qsymia (phentermine/topiramate). This drug combines phentermine with topiramate, an antiseizure medication. Patients receiving the recommended higher dose lost 22.5 pounds with some reported side effects including dry mouth, constipation, and insomnia.

Contrave, a combination of naltrexone, an anti-addiction medication with Wellbutrin (bupropion), an antidepressant, was approved in 2014. According to the manufacturer, weight loss averaged 25 pounds but about a third of the patients in the clinical trial experienced nausea. Later in that year, Saxenda (liraglutide), a once daily injectable drug developed for the treatment of type 2 diabetes was approved for treating obese individuals with at least one comorbid disorder. A task force of experts concluded:

> *Unfortunately, while they may be helpful, none of the drugs are "miracle cures." The Practice Guidelines[52] offered by The Endocrine Society and co-sponsored by the European Society of Endocrinology and The Obesity Society states, "Although all of these medications and others have been shown to be effective as adjunctive treatment, none have been shown to be effective on their own." (p. 8) The Guidelines also caution that, "Patients should be made aware that lifestyle changes are needed when using a weight loss medication. . ." (p. 8)*

You may need to remind your clients that, ultimately, lifestyle change is necessary even if they decide to try the medications. Chapters 4 - 11 will offer specific suggestions for making the lifestyle changes that are necessary for weight control.

SURGERY

It's estimated that 14.5 percent of the adult population in the US has a BMI of 35 or more. In addition to the health risks and behavioral problems, it's estimated that the health care expenses of severely obese individuals are almost twice that of their normal weight peers.[53] Given the modest weight losses resulting from pharmacological and lifestyle interventions, bariatric surgery is the most effective current treatment for severe obesity with over 200,000 procedures performed each year. Awareness of bariatric surgery increased as celebrities including Roseanne Barr and Al Roker have publicly discussed their experiences.

Many of your severely obese clients who have made repeated unsuccessful attempts to lose weight may have considered surgery, even if they can't afford it (typical cost is between $18,000 - $35,000) or have ambivalent feelings about it. You can help by providing information and clarifying some of the psychological issues that emerge with these procedures.

Currently, three bariatric procedures are widely used: adjustable gastric band (Lap Band), Roux-en-Y gastric bypass (RYGB), and vertical sleeve gastrectomy.

The laparoscopic adjustable gastric band procedure is the least invasive. The stomach and intestines remain intact but an adjustable silicone band is placed around the upper part of the stomach creating a pouch about the size of a golf ball. A thin tube connects the band to a port placed under the skin. Adding or removing saline through the port can adjust the band. Weight is lost gradually over two to three years since the smaller stomach pouch holds less food and there's delayed gastric emptying of partially digested food. A ten-year follow-up study of 714 patients found a 47 percent excess weight loss with no mortality associated with the procedure, although 40 percent needed some revision of the procedure and five percent had the band removed.[54] Frequent follow-up visits are typically required for adjustments and other studies have reported less favorable outcomes. As a result, the use of the gastric band procedure has decreased markedly in recent years.

With the Roux-en-Y a small stomach pouch, also about the size of a golf ball, is created and part of the small intestine is attached to the pouch. Food intake is limited by the small size of the pouch and less is absorbed because of the shortened intestine bypassing most of the stomach. Typically patients lose 60-70 percent of their excess weight.

Although Roux-en-Y is a major surgical procedure with possible complications, a ten-year follow-up found that 6.5 percent of the surgery patients had died compared with 13 percent of matched obese patients who did not have surgery.[55]

The vertical sleeve gastrectomy is a newer surgery that has become the most popular bariatric procedure. About 75 percent of the stomach is removed with the vertical sleeve gastrectomy leaving a banana-shaped stomach. No intestines are removed or bypassed. In addition to limiting the amount of food that can be consumed, appetite is reduced because there is less ghrelin, the hormone associated with hunger that is produced in the stomach. Typically there's less weight loss compared to the Roux-en-Y and the weight comes off more slowly, but this procedure may be preferred for patients who have severe heart or lung disease because the surgery has fewer risks than the Roux-en-Y procedure.

Despite the perception that these are dangerous procedures, a meta-analysis found a mortality of less than one percent, with weight losses of 44 to 66 pounds maintained for up to ten years.[56] A Swedish 15-year follow-up study found a 53 percent reduction in cardiovascular mortality and a 33 percent reduction in heart disease and stroke with the 20 percent post-surgical weight reduction. While the weight loss and reduction in mortality was beneficial, about 13 percent of the patients had postoperative complications.[57] Also, a significant number of patients have trouble maintaining their weight losses possibly as a result of psychological issues revolving around body weight.

In 2015, the FDA approved two balloon devices that are less invasive than surgery. Under mild sedation, the physician deposits a balloon in the stomach via the mouth and then fills it with saline so it expands creating a feeling of satiety. The balloon, used in conjunction with a diet and exercise program, is removed after six months. In one study, patients receiving the balloon lost an average of 14.3 pounds after six months and had an average weight loss of 9.9 pounds after a year although there were some reports of vomiting, nausea, and indigestion.[58]

Several years ago, I was confronted with an example of psychological issues that can affect the outcome of surgery. I gave a talk about emotional eating to an aftercare group for patients who'd had bariatric surgery. Afterwards, a young woman came up and confided that she'd been regaining weight after her procedure. Surprisingly she wasn't upset but rather seemed pleased with the weight gain. It was a brief conversation, so I don't know what the weight loss represented to her, but it illustrates that psychological issues involving weight might not be resolved by surgery. Even when the procedure has been successful, it can easily be defeated if the preexisting psychological issues have not been resolved. For example, the stomach pouch can be stretched by gradually increasing meal size. Frequent drinking of calorically dense liquids like milkshakes will also result in weight gain despite the small stomach.

If any of your patients are seriously considering a bariatric procedure, it's important that their expectations are realistic and they understand the post-surgical hazards and changes that will be necessary. Most bariatric programs require a psychological evaluation prior to surgery. Even if you are not doing the evaluation you should be aware of some of the possible contraindications.

Preexisting psychopathology, especially disordered eating, would predict poor postoperative outcomes. For example, about five percent of bariatric surgery candidates suffer from binge eating disorder. This has been associated with smaller post-surgical weight losses and possible gastrointestinal complications. While depressive symptoms often improve after surgery there is some evidence that depression and suicide may increase over time, especially for patients with a history of mood disorders. Also, while research findings are mixed, there are clinical reports of increased alcohol abuse following bariatric surgery.[59] Likewise, pre-existing marital conflict may not improve or could get worse after surgery.

Although it's not intended to be a bariatric procedure, some clients may be curious about liposuction for weight loss. While the idea of removing fat may be appealing, liposuction only affects subcutaneous fat. The procedure may improve the body's contours, but it won't alter the visceral fat that is responsible for much of your clients' excess weight and the health risks associated with obesity.

Bariatric surgery is not a magical procedure that will effortlessly remedy all weight troubles. One successful patient described it as "a tool, not a cure." If she hadn't made behavioral changes, been more active, and sought support from family and a therapist, she would have regained at least some of the weight. All surgery candidates should be informed about the post-operative changes that will be required. Patients will need to eat small meals, chew foods well and may feel the need to vomit when feeling full. They will need to avoid sugars and fats to prevent "dumping syndrome" which includes lightheadedness, nausea, sweating, cramping, and diarrhea. After surgery, they will need to take vitamins and engage in regular physical activity to maintain their weight loss.

Regardless if your client continues to diet, joins a structured program, tries one of the medications, or considers surgery, lifestyle changes will be necessary to maintain any weight loss. The remaining chapters will offer information that will enable you to help your client to make these changes.

ENDNOTES

33. Stunkard, A. J. & McLaren-Hume, M. (1959). The results of treatment for obesity: A review of the literature and report of a series. *AMA Archives of Internal Medicine, 103,* 79–85.

34. Herman, C. P. & Mack, D. (1975). Restrained and unrestrained eating. *Journal of Personality, 43,* 647–660.

35. Nutrition professor loses 27 pounds on junk food diet in 10 weeks (2010, Nov 8). *Medical News Today,* www.medicalnewstoday.com/articles/207071.php

36. Johnston, B. C., Kanters, S., Bandayrel, K., et al. (2014). Comparison of weight loss among named diet programs in overweight and obese adults: A meta-analysis. *JAMA, 312,* 923–933.

37. Raynor, H. A. & Epstein, L. H. (2001). Dietary variety, energy regulation, and obesity. *Psychological Bulletin, 127,* 325–341.

38. Division of Nutrition and Physical Activity (2006). Research to practice series no. 2: Portion size. Atlanta: Centers for Disease Control and Prevention.

39. Young, L. R. & Nestle, M. (1998). Variation in perceptions of a "medium" food portion: Implications for dietary guidance. *Journal of the American Dietetic Association, 98,* 458–459.

40. Shikany, J. M., Thomas, A. S., Beasley, T. M., Lewis, C. E. & Allison, D. B. (2013). Randomized controlled trial of the Medifast 5 & 1 Plan for weight loss. *International Journal of Obesity, 37,* 1571–1578.

41. Ditschuneit, H. H. & Flechtner-Mors, M. (2001). Value of Structured Meals for Weight Management: Risk Factors and Long-Term Weight Maintenance. *Obesity Research, 9,* 284S–289S.

42. Pinto, A. M., Fava, J. L., Hoffmann, D. A. & Wing, R. R. (2013). Combing behavioral weight loss treatment and a commercial program: A randomized clinical trial. *Obesity, 21,* 673–680.

43. Finkelstein, E. A. & Kruger, E. (2014). Meta- and cost-effectiveness analysis of commercial weight loss strategies. *Obesity, 22,* 1942–1951.

44. Mitchell, N. S., Dickinson, L. M., Kempe, A., & Tsai, A. G. (2011). Determining the effectiveness of Take Off Pounds Sensibly (TOPS), a nationally available nonprofit weight loss program. *Obesity, 19,* 568–573.

45. http://www.oa.org/pdfs/2010_Member_Survey.pdf.

46. Westphal, V. K & Smith, J. E. (1996). "Overeaters anonymous: Who goes and who succeeds?" *Eating Disorders 4*: 160–170.

47. Laing, B. Y., Mangione, C. M., Tseng, C. H. et al. (2014). Effectiveness of a smartphone application for weight loss compared with usual care in overweight primary care patients: A randomized, controlled trial. *Annals of Internal Medicine, 161 (10 Suppl),* S5–12.

48. Spring, B., Duncan, J. M., Janke, A. et al. (2013). Integrating technology into standard weight loss treatment: A randomized controlled trial. *JAMA Internal Medicine, 173,* 105–111.

49. Kodama, S., Saito, K., Tanaka, S. et al. (2012). Effect of web-based lifetyle modification on weight control: A meta analysis. *International Journal of Obesity, 36,* 675–685.

50. Pittler, M. H, Ernst, E. (2004). "Dietary supplements for body-weight reduction: A systematic review". *The American Journal of Clinical Nutrition 79,* 529–36.

51. Hendricks, E. J., Srisurapanont, M., Schmidt, S. L., Haggard, M., Souter, S., Mitchell, C. L., De Marco, D. G., Hendricks, M. J., Istratiy, Y. & Greenway, F. L. (2014). Addiction potential of phentermine prescribed during long-term treatment of obesity. *International Journal of Obesity, 38,* 292–298.

52. Apovian, C. M., Aronne, L. J., Bessesen, D. H. et al. (2015). Pharmacological management of obesity: An Endocrine Society Clinical Practice Guideline. *The Journal of Clinical Endocrinology and Metabolism,* 100, 342–362.

53. Arterburn, D. E. & Fisher, D. P. (2014). The current state of the evidence for bariatric surgery. *JAMA, 312,* 898–899.

54. O'Brien, P. E., MacDonald, L., Anderson, M. Brennan, L, & Brown, W. A. (2013). Long-term outcomes after bariatric surgery: Fifteen-year follow-up of adjustable gastric banding and a systematic review of the bariatric surgical literature. *Annals of Surgery, 257,* 87–94.

55. Guidry, C. A., Davies, S. W., Sawyer, R. G., Schirmer, B. D. & Hallowell, P. T. (in press). Gastric bypass improves survival compared with propensity-matched controls: A cohort study with over 10-year follow-up. *American Journal of Surgery.*

56. Maggard, M., Shugarman, L. R., Suttorp, M. et al. (2005). Meta-analysis: surgical treatment of obesity. *Annals of Internal Medicine, 142,* 547–559.

57. Sjostrom, L., Peltonen, M., Jacobson, P. et al. (2012). Bariatric surgery and long-term cardiovascular events. *JAMA, 307,* 56–65.

58. Lowes, R. (2015, Jul 28). FDA approves ReShape dual balloon device to treat obesity. *Medscape,* http://www.medscape.com/viewarticle/848767

59. Sarwer, D. B. (2014). Decreasing readmission through psychological evaluation and treatment. *Surgery for Obesity and Related Diseases, 10,* 389–391.

Chapter 4

Why Are You Eating That?
– Physical Hunger

"Never go grocery shopping when you're hungry." You've probably read this advice dozens of times in diet books and magazine articles. There's research to support this recommendation. Hunger makes food more attractive and motivates people to spend money and time to get it.

A recent study shows that hunger can influence more than food purchases; it can have an effect on all shopping. In one experiment, researchers found that hunger even increased purchases of non-food items like binder clips.[60] In another study, shoppers checking out at a department store were asked how hungry they were prior to scanning their receipts. Hungry shoppers bought more non-food items and spent more money than less hungry shoppers.[61]

So now there's another reason to avoid getting hungry - you'll spend less. Hunger is a powerful motivator, so how can you help clients avoid getting hungry without eating more?

IS IT REALLY HUNGER?

According to Dr. Brian Wansink, director of the Cornell Food and Brand Lab, the average person makes 200 or more eating decisions a day. Corn Flakes or Oatmeal? More or less salt? Add or skip dessert? Drink the coffee black or add half and half? We do this about 200 times a day but, if you asked your client, "Why are you eating that?" it's quite likely that he would answer, "Because I'm hungry." Yet for most clients physical hunger accounts for only a small portion of the eating decisions they will make each day. The external cues, thoughts, emotions and relationships discussed in Chapters 5 - 7 will determine most of their daily eating decisions. You can ask your client a few simple questions to help him determine if the desire to eat was triggered by true physical hunger rather than external cues, thoughts or emotions. The questions are:

1. How long had it been since the last meal or snack?	1. If it's less than 3 hours it probably wasn't triggered by physical hunger.
2. Where you hungry for anything in particular or would any palatable food satisfy the hunger?	2. If it was physical hunger any palatable food would do. Although in rare instances cravings may result from a nutritional deficiency when a specific food is craved it probably isn't physical hunger.
3. Did the hunger come on suddenly or develop gradually.	3. Physical hunger develops over time. A sudden desire to eat has other causes.
4. When you felt hungry, were you hungry at that moment or were you expecting to be hungry later?	4. If the current goal is to prevent hunger later the eating isn't physical hunger.

Even if physical hunger is responsible for a minority of eating decisions, it's still important to understand it. Some of your clients, primarily men, will report difficulty managing their weight because they are frequently hungry. You can help them develop methods to satisfy their hunger while maintaining a healthy weight.

Hunger is a complicated phenomenon involving physiological and metabolic events, neurotransmitters and brain activity, hormones and behaviors. It's generally seen as an unpleasant sensation associated with stomach contractions (hunger pangs), light-headedness or dizziness, weakness, irritability, and difficulty concentrating. Hunger is triggered by high levels of ghrelin, a hormone that is produced in the stomach that is frequently accompanied by the stomach contractions. Both leptin, a hormone produced by fat cells throughout the body, and peptide YY from cells in the intestines, are released after eating, causing the hunger to subside while feelings of satiety or comfortable fullness increase, but this process is not immediate; it typically it takes about 20 minutes to start.

Before giving your client advice on coping with hunger, consider the role that eating might play in sex role identification. Traditionally women are dainty eaters. In social settings they're likely to order small portions, and leave some food on their plate because they're full. Heartily eating large portions wouldn't be lady-like. In contrast, men may express their masculinity by ordering a large portion, finishing everything on the plate, asking for seconds and then bragging about it later. One father told me about eating at a buffet restaurant with his teenaged son. With great pride, he recounted how the server incredulously asked his son, "Are you back again?" Another client, described himself as a "big eater." Although he was concerned about his obesity, eating large amounts of food was an integral part of his self-concept.

If your client seems to take pride in eating large amounts, a direct challenge is likely to result in a defensive response. Instead, you can help these clients by suggesting methods for coping with their hunger while minimizing their caloric intake.

Culture can also play a role in your client's judgments of hunger. For example, minority cultures with a history of food insecurity may view large servings as standard when food is available. You could ask your client about family traditions and lessons regarding eating that he learned in childhood.

PORTION DISTORTION

For the first 60 years of its existence, Coca Cola came in just one size, a six and a half ounce bottle. Later, when a 16-ounce bottle was available, it was advertised as providing three servings. Now most of your clients would feel like a cheapskate if they shared the 16-ounce bottle with two friends.

As a culture, we've grown accustomed to ever-larger portions and might feel deprived if we had to eat smaller amounts. The increase in portion size was clearly demonstrated by a 2009 study of cookbooks.[62] Cornell University researchers compared 18 recipes in *The Joy of Cooking* published in 2006 with the same recipes found in the first edition of the cookbook published in 1936. Portion sizes for these homemade foods have increased markedly in the 70-year interval between editions. For example, the chicken gumbo recipe went from making 14 servings at 228 calories each to making 10 servings at 576 calories each. Although some of the increase was the result of changes in ingredients, most of the difference was due to larger portion size. Larger portions might not be a problem if there was less eating at subsequent meals, but the evidence suggests that when people overeat at a meal they won't compensate later for their increased consumption. They'll eat just as much, or possibly more at later meals.

How can your client reduce portion size but still feel satisfied? He might object if you just told him to eat less. Instead suggest that your client focus on the physical sensations of hunger and rate them on a 1-10 scale where 1 = low hunger while 10 = extreme hunger. As he becomes more aware, he'll recognize that it isn't necessary to eat every time he thinks he might be hungry. It's best to eat when experiencing moderate hunger (4 - 6) rather than eating with little or no hunger or waiting until the hunger is more intense and likely to result in rapid overeating.

Assuming he isn't physically hungry (if he is, check the section on Snacking on page 42) most likely he is eating for the pleasure the food provides. Research demonstrates that most of the pleasure of eating comes in the first few bites. Chapter 11 offers several practical suggestions for using mindful eating to maximize the enjoyment of eating so that your client will be satisfied with smaller amounts.

THE GREAT BREAKFAST CONTROVERSY

Many chronic dieters will skip breakfast because they're trying to lose weight. When I encourage eating breakfast, I often hear objections. For example, a client would say,

> *I'm not hungry when I wake up, so why should I make myself eat 300 calories that I don't want? Besides, I have to get the kids off to school and get myself ready for work, so I don't have the time.*

Despite the opposition, I encourage clients to have breakfast even if it means taking a container of Cheerios, a banana, a slice of cheese, and milk to work and having breakfast at their desk. This will prevent hunger that can lead to rapid overeating at the next meal. I'll remind clients that it's more difficult to control eating when they're very hungry. It takes about 20 minutes before their hunger will start to be satisfied so, if they're very hungry, when they finally do eat, they'll eat rapidly and consume more than they need before they feel satisfied.

There's conflicting research findings about breakfast. A study of 20,000 men found that eating breakfast ". . .may modestly contribute to the prevention of weight gain as compared with skipping breakfast. . ." (p. 2463).[63] In contrast, a study of 283 obese or overweight individuals trying to lose weight compared a group who were told to eat breakfast with another group told to skip breakfast. After 16 weeks, there was no difference in weight loss between groups.[64] Despite the conflicting evidence, I still encourage eating breakfast. While there may be no weight loss over 16 weeks, longer-term there may be benefits. Another benefit of breakfast is that it helps establish a pattern of having regular meals rather than haphazard snacking.

When promoting breakfast, it's important to recommend solid foods rather than a breakfast drink. Research shows that consuming a meal as a liquid is less satiating than consuming the same meal as a solid. A recent study found that approximately 80 percent of the participants given a liquid meal wanted to consume more to alleviate their hunger.[65] Also you can encourage your clients to include protein rich foods like eggs and dairy in their breakfast since protein burns more calories and promotes more satiety than carbohydrates or fat.[66]

SLEEPING AND EATING

Ask your weight conscious clients about their sleep habits. There is substantial evidence linking sleep deprivation to increased hunger and eating. If they report sleep difficulties you can ask them:

- Do they work the night shift, watch late night TV shows, or surf the web before bed?
- If they're tired, do they take a nap in the daytime?
- Do they drink coffee, tea, colas, or energy drinks in the late afternoon or evening?
- Do they use alcohol as a way to relax before going to sleep?
- Do they take pride in being able to function on only a few hours of sleep?

Before World War I, Americans averaged between 8.7 to 9 hours of sleep per night. In a 2008 poll, the average was six hours and 40 minutes. The same survey found that 41 percent of respondents who slept six hours or less on weeknights were obese versus 28 percent who slept eight or more hours.[67] Lack of sleep may be partially responsible for the current obesity epidemic!

Sleep deprivation results in subjective reports of hunger, especially for calorically dense foods. Also being tired decreases physical activity and may reduce the ability to resist tempting foods. In addition to the psychological consequences of tiredness, there's a direct effect of sleep deprivation on metabolic hormones. Lack of sleep causes increased ghrelin secretion and lower levels of leptin (remember, ghrelin is associated with hunger, leptin with satiety). Although chronic insomnia would require specialized treatment, you can help your client develop good sleep hygiene and decrease hunger. Here are some suggestions you can offer:

- Establish a sleep routine. Go to bed about the same time each night.

- Even when tired, don't nap during the daytime.

- Turn off the TV, cell phone, and computer at least one hour before going to sleep because the electroluminescent light from these screens delays production of the sleep regulating hormone melatonin for up to two hours.

- Avoid caffeinated drinks in the afternoon and evening. Caffeine is metabolized very slowly, and remains in the body for up to 36 hours.

- Avoid alcoholic beverages after dinner. While it might feel relaxing, alcohol interferes with REM sleep causing more awakenings and restless sleep.

- Use white noise (e.g., an air conditioner, white noise smart phone app) to shield ambient noise.

- Limit time in bed to sleeping and sex.

- A glass of warm milk or non-caffeine tea before bedtime can be soothing.

- Physical activity during the day helps reduce stress and improves sleep, but not immediately before going to bed.

For additional information about the physical effects of insomnia, sleep requirements by age, and methods for improving sleep, visit the National Sleep Foundation website (www.sleepfoundation.org).

SNACKING

If your client has lunch at noon and doesn't eat anything until dinner at 6:30 or 7:00, he's going to be hungry and have the same difficulty controlling his eating as the breakfast skipper does. Having a mid-afternoon snack is a reasonable solution to this problem, but before you suggest snacking, it's helpful to make a distinction between a snack vs. a treat. A treat is something that you eat for pure enjoyment. Ice cream, chocolate, and candy can be treats. Typically treats have little nutritional value and are calorically dense.

For many of your clients, their favorite treat is chocolate. Although it's calorically dense, laden with sugar and fat, it does NOT need to be forbidden, only limited. This may seem to be a problem for some women who identify themselves as "chocoholics" but there's little evidence to suggest that chocolate is physiologically addicting. In one study, 40 percent of American women reported craving chocolate perimenstrually in contrast to four percent of Spanish women.[68] These findings suggest that there's a cultural rather than a physiological basis for chocolate craving. It's possible that some of the appeal of chocolate comes from its associations with love. For example, frequent Valentines' Day gifts in the U.S. are heart-shaped boxes of chocolates.

Regardless of the reasons, chocolate craving can be satisfied without causing significant weight gain. Your client can have her chocolate simply by using it as an after dinner dessert rather than as a snack between meals. When she's finished her dinner, she won't be hungry so there will be less likelihood that she'll eat the chocolate quickly. Also dessert is accepted as part of a meal, so she needn't feel guilty about having the chocolate. Without hunger and guilt she can eat the chocolate slowly, focusing on enjoying the sensations that chocolate provides. You can use the suggestions for mindful eating presented in Chapter 11 to help your client enhance her enjoyment of chocolate so that she'll be satisfied with a small amount.

Unlike chocolate or other treats, a snack is something to eat between meals to stave off hunger. A snack shouldn't be random nibbling on whatever is convenient (often found in vending machines) but rather it should be planned. The snack food should be appetizing even if it isn't your client's favorite treat. Fruit, prewashed baby carrots, cheese slices, and especially nuts make good snacks. Studies have demonstrated that greater frequency of nut consumption was associated with increased satiation and lower BMI. Some evidence also suggests that chronic nut consumption is associated with elevated basal metabolism.[69] A carefully controlled study of breakfast shakes containing either walnuts or a placebo found increased levels of satiety and sense of fullness with the walnut shake.[70] Since nuts are high in fat and calorically dense, you should advise your clients to limit their snacking to a handful of nuts. One handful should be enough to keep the hunger at bay until dinnertime.

Although a mid-afternoon snack can help regulate eating later in the day, the frequently cited advice to increase meal frequency by having six mini-meals rather than the conventional breakfast, lunch, and dinner is misguided. In several studies, increasing meal frequency reduced feelings of satiety and did not result in greater weight loss.[71] It's likely that the more frequent exposure to food increases the desire to eat (more on this in Chapter 5).

BULK, NOT CALORIES

If you were very hungry and you could only choose between one Oreo cookie or a pound of spinach, which would do a better job of satisfying your hunger? While a pound of spinach might not sound too appetizing, it probably would be more filling than the cookie, even though they have the same number of calories. This illustrates an important point for your clients who report that they need large amounts of food to feel satisfied. It's food bulk, not the number of calories that creates satiety.

Dr. Barbara Rolls, a professor of nutrition at Penn State, developed a strategy she calls Volumetrics[72] for feeling full without overeating. She notes that, for 100 calories you could have one-quarter cup of raisins or almost two cups of grapes. The grapes would be more filling even though the difference between grapes and raisins is water content; raisins are just dried grapes. While drinking water by itself probably won't decrease hunger, eating foods that have a high water content will increase satiety without adding many calories. The same principle applies for foods rich in fiber. Fiber-rich foods like beans and whole grains add bulk thereby increasing satiety without adding many calories. This approach is different from low fat dieting, since many low fat or no-fat foods are still calorically dense. Often when fat is removed, the foods taste terrible so sugar is added to make it palatable. The result is that many fat-free foods like pretzels or crackers are still calorically dense.

One unusual feature of the Volumetrics approach is that instead of just restricting food choices like most diets, it suggests adding vegetables and other foods high in water or fiber content to recipes. For example, by putting fruit on cereal, apple slices in chicken salad, salsa on chicken, vegetables in marinara sauce, or eggplant in lasagna, the caloric density of the dish would be reduced. This was demonstrated in a study where participants ate in a lab once a week for three weeks. They could eat as much as they wanted but didn't know that on some days the cooks added pureed vegetables to the main dish so that it looked identical but had 25 percent fewer calories. With the pureed vegetables participants consumed as much as 360 fewer calories.[73] By adding vegetables to recipes, your client would be able to eat his usual portion even though the caloric intake was reduced.

Recall that it takes about 20 minutes after starting a meal before feeling full. Dr. Rolls suggests starting a meal with soup or salad (without creamy dressing or croutons) waiting a few minutes and then serving the main course. In one of Dr. Rolls' studies, women were given a chicken rice casserole on some days while on other days they got the same casserole with 10 ounces of water cooked in to make it soup. When they had the soup, they consumed about 100 fewer calories at lunch, weren't hungrier later, and didn't eat more at dinner.[74]

Once your client learns how to reduce the caloric density of his meals, he can continue to be a "big eater" and satisfy his large appetite without gaining weight. Even if your client isn't a self-described "big eater" he can still decrease eating by having breakfast, getting a good night's sleep, and having some nuts as a snack in the afternoon.

ENDNOTES

60. Xu, A. J., Schwarz, N. & Wyler, R. S. (2015). Hunger promotes acquisition of nonfood objects. *PNAS Early Edition,* www.pnas.org/cgi/doi/10.1073/pnas.1417712112. Accessed April 19, 2016.

61. Xu, A. J., Schwarz, N. & Wyer, R. S. (2015). Hunger promotes acquisition of nonfood objects. *PNAS Early Edition,* www.pnas.org/cgi/doi/10.1073/pnas.1417712112

62. Wansink, B., & Payne, C. R. (2009). The *Joy of Cooking* too much: 70 years of calorie increases in classic recipes. *Annals of Internal Medicine, 150,* 291.

63. van der Heijen, A. A. W. A., Hu, F. B., Rimm, E. B., & van Dam, R. M. (2007). A prospective study of breakfast consumption and weight gain among U.S. men. *Obesity, 15,* 2463–2469.

64. Dhurandhar, E. J., Dawson, J., Alcorn, A., Larsen, L. H. et al. (2014). The effectiveness of breakfast recommendations on weight loss: a randomized controlled trial. *American Journal of Clinical Nutrition, 100,* 507–513.

65. Martens, M. J. I., Westerterp-Plantenga, M. S. (2012). Mode of consumption plays a role in alleviating hunger and thirst. *Obesity, 20,* 517–524.

66. Acheson, K. J. et al. (2011). Protein choices targeting thermogenesis and metabolism. *American Journal of Clinical Nutrition, 93,* 525–534.

67. National Sleep Foundation. (2008). 2008 sleep in America poll. March 2, 2008, http://sleepfoundation.org/sites/default/files/2008%20POLL%20SOF.PDF

68. Zellner, D. A., Garriga-Trillo, A., Centeno, S. & Wadsworth, E. (2004). Chocolate craving and the menstrual cycle. *Appetite, 42,* 119–121.

69. Mattes, R. D., Kris-Etherton, P. M. & Foster G. D. (2008). Impact of peanuts and tree nuts on body weight and healthy weight loss in adults. *Journal of Nutrition, 138,* 1741S–1745S.

70. Brennan, A. M., Sweeney, L. L., Liu, X., & Mantzoros, C. S. (2009). Walnut consumption increases satiation but has no effect on insulin resistance or the metabolic profile over a 4-day period. *Obesity, 18,* 1176–1182.

71. Ohkawara, K., Cornier, M., Kohrt, W. M. & Melanson, E. L. (2013). Effects of increased meal frequency on fat oxidation and perceived hunger. *Obesity, 21,* 336–343.

72. Rolls, B. & Barnett, R. A. (2003). *The volumetrics weight-control plan.* New York: Harper Torch.

73. Blatt, A., Roe, L., Rolls, B. (2011). Hidden vegetables: An effective strategy to reduce energy intake and increase vegetable intake in adults. *American Journal of Clinical Nutrition, 93,* 756–763.

74. Rolls, B. J., Bell, E. A., & Thorwart, M. L. (1999). Water incorporated into a food but not served with a food decreases energy intake in lean women. *American Journal of Clinical Nutrition, 70,* 448–455.

Chapter 5

Why Are You Eating That? *– External Cues*

It's 8:30 PM, and your client is watching TV when a commercial for Doritos comes on. Without thinking, she heads to the kitchen looking for something crunchy to eat. She had dinner less than two hours ago, so she's not physically hungry, yet she feels the need to eat and grabs a bag of chips and starts munching away. The TV commercial is one of the dozens of external cues that can trigger unnecessary eating, often without awareness. While the relationship between the commercial and your client's desire to eat is obvious, the external cues that can prompt eating are frequently much more subtle.

SUBTLE CUES CAN TRIGGER EATING

Melody, a 47-year-old teacher in one of my weight control groups, provides a good example of subtle cues triggering eating. On school days, she would leave work around 3:30 in the afternoon and use the take-out window at Taco Bell to get a burrito to "tide me over" till dinner, typically at 7:00. One afternoon, she had to take a detour because there was construction on the road she usually used. That night as she sat down to dinner it occurred to her that she hadn't had her afternoon burrito. She hadn't missed the burrito; in the absence of the external cue - the Taco Bell - she didn't have the urge to eat.

Melody wasn't aware of the effect the external cue (the sight of the Taco Bell) had on her eating, but this is typical. In a study conducted at Cornell, 192 people overate as a result of having been given a large bowl of food. Although they ate more food, 21 percent of the participants denied eating more, while 75 percent who recognized that they'd had a lot to eat attributed their overeating to hunger. Only 4 percent recognized that they ate more because they were given more food.[75] The findings demonstrate that people frequently don't recognize when they overeat, but even when they

47

are aware that they've eaten too much, they rarely recognize the reasons why they overate. You can help your clients become aware of the cues that prompt unnecessary eating so they can alter their environment to eliminate or reduce the effects of these external cues.

THE SEE-FOOD DIET

The sight of food in front of you is probably the most potent external cue. Dr. Brian Wansink, the Director of Cornell's Brand and Food Lab, has done several ingenious studies demonstrating that, independent of physical hunger, people eat more when more food is readily available.

In a now classic study, Wansink had 62 college students come to his lab to have Campbell's tomato soup for lunch. Half of the students had normal soup bowls; the other half had bottomless bowls. The bottomless bowls had a hole drilled in the bottom and a hole in the table so that a tube could connect the bowl to a six-quart pot of hot soup. As the students ate soup, the bowl automatically refilled itself. Students with the bottomless bowls ate 73 percent more soup. Although they thought they had only consumed 127 calories, their actual consumption averaged 268 calories. Their estimates were about the same as the estimates of their peers with regular bowls. In other words, they weren't aware of how much more they were eating.[76]

Although your clients are unlikely to encounter bottomless soup bowls, the size of the bowls, plates, and glasses that they use may determine how much they eat and drink. Several studies have shown that people eat more when using bigger plates and drink more with wide glasses rather than tall glasses.[77] This can be a special problem for the 54 percent of Americans who admit that they clean their plates regardless of the quantity of food in front of them.[78]

The potency of visual cues is not just limited to mealtime. In another study, Wansink gave moviegoers a free soft drink and either a medium-sized or large bucket of popcorn. What the recipients didn't know was that the popcorn was stale, having been popped five days earlier. Even though it tasted like Styrofoam, the folks who got the larger bucket still ate 53 percent more.[79] Interestingly, after the movie was over and participants were told about the tendency to eat more when given larger servings, most thought that they couldn't be fooled, it didn't apply to them. Most likely your clients aren't aware, and may deny, that visual cues influence their eating.

There are dozens of visual cues that could trigger eating. Watching other people eat, seeing food in transparent containers, viewing TV commercials, billboards, even the color of the plate can increase eating (there's less consumption when the plate contrasts with the food color).

The obvious conclusion from Wansink's studies is that, whether we know it or not, we're all on the See-Food Diet; when we see food within reach, we eat more. Instead of encouraging your clients to have the will power to resist temptations, they can alter their environment to decrease the visual cues. Here are some suggestions:

- At meals, serve reasonable portions of food in the kitchen and bring the plates to the dining table instead of setting serving bowls and platters on the table.
- Use salad plates rather than dinner plates for meals and tall, rather than wide glasses.
- Remove food from every room except the kitchen.
- Use opaque containers rather than clear plastic wrap for attractive leftovers.
- When buying calorically dense treats, choose single servings rather than bulk containers (e.g., ice cream cups or sandwiches rather than half gallon cartons).

Seeing food is not the only visual cue that can trigger unnecessary eating. Melody didn't need to see the burrito; she only had to see the Taco Bell restaurant, a visual cue that was associated with the burrito. Unfortunately, it's virtually impossible to avoid all the cues in the environment that are associated with eating. In addition to the restaurants they drive by, there are TV commercials, magazine ads for rich foods (in between the articles on dieting), candy on co-workers' desks, and dozens of other cues in your clients' environments. While your client can't modify the larger environment, increasing her awareness of the visual cues will make eating less likely.

The See-Food Diet also includes the sense of smell. If you've ever walked by a Mrs. Field's cookies stand or a Cinnabon bakery in a mall and taken a deep breath, you'll recognize the link between an appealing aroma and the desire to eat. Closer to home, can you recall smells coming from the kitchen when your mother or father was preparing a favorite meal? While you wouldn't want to deprive your clients of the pleasant smell that is an integral part of enjoying tasty food, becoming aware of the effects of smell on the desire to eat will help them make the response less automatic.

SEE-FOOD EATING OUT

In the 23 years from 1977 to 2000, the number of meals consumed at home decreased by 42 percent[80] with one quarter of American adults eating fast food every day. A typical fast food meal contains 200 more calories than a home cooked meal.[81] It's common to find restaurant meals that will provide a whole day's worth of calories in a single sitting. For example, you could have a 2000-calorie meal at Chipotle; a carnitas burrito with a Coke and side of guacamole and chips, or if you go upscale, you could have a 2000-calorie ribeye steak and martini at Ruth's Chris Steak House.

When your client is eating out, he can be tempted to eat more even before the food arrives. In one study, restaurant menus were manipulated so on some days the foods were given a simple descriptive label (e.g., Seafood Filet), while on other days, the same food was called Succulent Italian Seafood Filet. Although it was the same food, offered at the same price, the more descriptive title increased sales by 27 percent.[82]

IT'S DINNERTIME

The clock can be a potent external cue. Simply knowing that it's mealtime can provoke eating regardless of physical hunger. In a clever study of two amnesiac patients (i.e., they couldn't remember events that occurred more than a minute earlier), University of Pennsylvania psychologists told the patients that it was lunchtime even though they had finished a meal 30 minutes earlier. They readily consumed the second lunch, and started on a third lunch when it was offered later.[83]

You can ask your client if they ever "forgot" that they were full but had a meal anyway just because it was dinnertime. Perhaps they were at a late afternoon social gathering, helped themselves to a plateful of appetizers along with their drinks, and then had a full meal when they got home. The habit of eating lunch or dinner at a regular time can trigger eating in the absence of physical hunger.

MAKING EATING TREATS EFFORTFUL

Research has demonstrated that, as the effort required to obtain food increases, the amount consumed decreases. For example, one study found that having to slide open the glass lid of an ice cream freezer in a cafeteria resulted in 14 percent of the patrons buying ice cream. When the lid was already open,

30 percent bought the ice cream.[84] In another study, candy dishes with 30 Hershey's Kisses were placed either on the corner of secretaries desks, in the top drawer of the desk, or on a file cabinet about six feet from the desk. On average the secretaries ate nine Kisses if they were in sight, sitting on the desk, six Kisses if they were in the desk drawer, but only four if they were six feet away.[85]

The practical implication of these findings is that it isn't necessary to completely prohibit calorically dense treats, just make them less visible and more difficult to get. Ask your client how she can rearrange her environment to make it less convenient to eat favorite treats. Could she store tempting foods on top shelves of cabinets or bottom shelves of the refrigerator? Instead of buying brownies, could she buy brownie mix? If she needs to keep treats in the house, she could buy treats that require preparation and can only be eaten with utensils rather than directly out of the container.

MAGIC WORDS

"Low fat," "All natural," "Gluten free," "Organic," "No trans fats," "Vegan," "Non-GMO." You've seen these terms hundreds of times on food wrappers. The implication is that the food inside is good for your health. Whether there's any validity to the implied health benefit is a topic for nutritionists to study, but for your weight conscious clients, any of these terms may be a license to eat more of the food. This is known as a "health halo;" when one aspect of the food is seen as healthy, it conveys permission to eat more. In an informal survey, people were shown either pictures of a restaurant meal or pictures of the same meal with the addition of two crackers that were labeled "Trans Fat Free." They were asked to estimate the number of calories in the meal. Although the crackers actually added 100 calories, the estimates with the crackers were 199 calories lower than for the cracker-free meal.[86]

The effects of a health halo can have a significant impact when eating meals away from home. For example, Subway restaurants are widely seen as offering healthier, lower calorie meals than McDonald's. Research participants who had eaten at least three times in both restaurants estimated that the Subway sandwich (12-inch turkey) had 200 fewer calories than the McDonald's Big Mac although they both had 600 calories. In a related study, participants given the opportunity to order drinks and a side order were more likely to upgrade to a larger soda and choose cookies when the main course was a Subway sandwich rather than a Big Mac. Apparently, being virtuous by eating a "healthier" sandwich allowed for an indulgence resulting in the consumption of additional calories. The researchers suggest a simple strategy for countering the effects of a health halo. When the participants were instructed to consider that the health claims might not be true, the halo disappeared.[87]

These counterintuitive findings suggest that we should ask clients if they are trying to "eat healthy" and follow up with a request for more details. Be careful to avoid making your client feel foolish but you can describe the health halo and suggest that what appears to be healthier might not be lower in calories.

MULTITASKING WITH FOOD

Ask your client to describe a typical mealtime. What are they doing while eating? Often the TV is on, but they could also be reading, talking on the phone, scanning their emails on their smartphones, driving in their car, texting, etc. etc. One poll found that 91 percent of respondents watch TV while eating, 35 percent eat lunch at their desk at work, and 26 percent eat while driving.[88] While your client might explain this behavior as an attempt to be more efficient or productive, it's not likely that having the TV on while eating increases productivity or that his schedule never allows for an uninterrupted meal. One possible motivation for your weight conscious client, especially if he is a habitual dieter, is to distract himself with TV or other activities to avoid feeling guilty when eating.

Despite work demands, overscheduled activities, or guilty feelings, it's important to reduce extraneous stimulation so that your client can focus on eating. Research demonstrates that watching TV lessens control of eating, decreases attention to the sensations provided by the food, and increases the amount of food consumed.[89] While this finding seems self-evident, your client may still resist, complaining that it feels awkward to eat without the TV. One of my clients, a 52-year-old, married bank executive, had started to lose weight when I suggested turning off the TV during mealtimes. At our next session, she reported that she missed the TV at dinner and her husband and son complained. I agreed to a more gradual approach rather than going "cold turkey" so that, over a few weeks, she was able to wean the family off viewing while eating.

Although television viewing while eating is probably the most common distraction, you'll find that your clients have many other activities that decrease their awareness of their eating which results in increased consumption. Ask your client to keep track of their mealtime activities. If she's like most multitasking eaters, making eating a singular activity will feel unnatural, so it's best to approach this change gradually. Starting with one meal, or if necessary, for the first three or five minutes of the meal, have your client refrain from any activity other than eating and conversing. Ask her to tell you what the experience felt like. Often, this discussion will provide a useful starting point for the exploration of her feelings about eating and weight.

RITUALS AND ROUTINES

When Charles came home from work, he walked in the door and went straight to the pantry where he helped himself to two cookies as a reward for having made it through the day. If it was a particularly stressful day, he might have three or four cookies. This daily routine added about 700 calories per week or a 10-pound weight gain in a year. Other common eating rituals include popcorn at the movies, coffee and doughnuts during a morning break at work, milk and cookies after school, and snacking while watching television. Often these rituals become so routine they don't register as unnecessary eating. You can help your client identify similar rituals and plan alternatives that don't involve eating. For example, Charles enjoyed playing a videogame on his iPad, but felt that this was a waste of time so he only played on weekends. With some discussion, he was able to substitute this guilty pleasure for eating as a reward when he came home from work.

Jennifer usually grabbed a snack when she sat down to watch TV in the evening. When we reviewed her evening rituals, she decided that she could brush and floss her teeth immediately after dinner. Knowing that if she snacked while watching, she'd need to brush and floss again was sufficient to control snacking. Perhaps your client could knit while watching movies or TV, allow herself to spend guilt-free time on a hobby, read, or find an activity that keeps the hands busy to substitute for snacking.

THE END OF WILLPOWER

Consistent with the widely held negative views of obesity, the solution that is often proposed is to just to exert more will power. According to this view, by applying will power the overweight individual will be able to overcome temptation, eat less, and lose weight. Of course, this oversimplification completely ignores the biological aspects of weight regulation and contributes to stigmatization. Even if we ignore biology and just focus on the psychology of eating, telling your client that he needs to exercise will power is not helpful.

Dr. Roy Baumeister summarized the findings of many research studies of willpower. He concluded:

- *You have a finite amount of willpower that becomes depleted as you use it.*
- *You use the same stock of willpower for all manner of tasks.*[90]

In other words, if your client uses some will power at work by not telling her boss what she really thinks of him, and uses more when she's dealing with traffic on the way home, and still more dealing with demanding kids when she gets home, your client won't have a lot of will power left to resist tempting snacks when she finally gets to relax and watch TV. Instead of relying on your client's finite supply of willpower to reduce eating, she can use some of the suggestions in this chapter to alter her environment to minimize the cues that trigger eating. With fewer cues, will power won't be necessary.

ENDNOTES

75. Wansink, B. & Sobal, J. (2007). The 200 daily food decisions we overlook. *Environment and Behavior, 39,* 106–123.
76. Wansink, B., Painter, J. E., & North, J. (2005). Bottomless bowls: Why visual cues of portion size may influence intake. *Obesity Research, 13,* 93–100.
77. Chandon, P. & Wansink, B. (2012). Does food marketing need to make us fat? A review and solutions. *Nutrition Reviews, 70,* 571–593.
78. Collins, K. (2006). New survey on portion size: Washington DC: American Institute for Cancer Research.
79. Wansink, B. & Park, S. (2001). At the movies: How external cues and perceived taste impact consumption volume. *Food Quality and Preference, 12,* 69–74.
80. Johnson, N. G. (2003). Psychology and health: Research, practice, and policy. *American Psychologist, 58,* 670–677.
81. Bowman, S. A. & Vinyard, B. T. (2004). Fast food consumption of U.S. adults: Impact on energy and nutrient intakes and overweight status. *Journal of the American College of Nutrition, 2,* 163–168.
82. Wansink, B., Painter, J. E., & van Ittersum, K. (2001). Descriptive menu labels' effect on sales. *Cornell Hotel and Restaurant Administrative Quarterly, 42,* 68–72.
83. Rozin, P., Dow, S., Moscovitch, M., & Rajaram, S. (1998). What causes humans to begin and end a meal? A role for memory for what has been eaten, as evidenced by a study of multiple meal eating in amnesic patients. *Psychological Science, 9,* 392–396.

84. Meyers, A. W., Stunkard, A. J. & Coll, M. (1980). Food accessibility and food choice. *Archives of General Psychiatry, 37,* 1133–1135.

85. Painter, J. E., Wansink, B., & Hieggelke, J. B. (2001). How visibility and convenience influence candy consumption. *Appetite, 38,* 237–238.

86. Tierney, J. (2008, December 2). Health halo can hide the calories. *The New York Times,* p. D-1.

87. Chandon, P. & Wansink, B. (2007). The biasing health halos of fast-food restaurant health claims: Lower calorie estimates and higher side-dish consumption intentions. *Journal of Consumer Research, 34,* 301–314.

88. Wansink, B. (2006). *Mindless eating: Why we eat more than we think.* New York: Bantam, p. 104.

89. Hetherington, M. M., Anderson, A. S., Norton, G. N. M., et al. (2006). Situational effects on meal intake: A comparison of eating alone and eating with others. *Physiology & Behavior, 88,* 498–505.

90. Baumeister, R. F. & Tierney, J. (2011). *Willpower: Rediscovering the greatest human strength.* New York: Penguin, p.35.

Chapter 6

Why Are You Eating That?
– *Emotions*

Gail was a 39-year-old, single, depressed, bank employee. She weighed 270 pounds (BMI = 42.3). She reported that she'd often have a Marie Callender's pie with soda for dinner, sometimes overeating until she was physically ill. She reported that when she binges on candy she "doesn't care because it's comforting."

Gail's depression-related bingeing is an extreme example of emotions triggering eating. It meets the DSM-5® (Diagnostic and Statistical Manual of Mental Disorders, Fifth Edition)[91] criteria for Binge Eating Disorder, but less severe eating in response to emotions is far more common. For example, a study in the journal, *Psychological Science* reported that on Monday, after an NFL football game, fans of losing teams ate ten percent more calories while fans of the winning team decreased their caloric consumption by five percent. In cities with an NFL team that didn't play, there was no change in eating.[92] It's likely that most of the disappointed fans didn't have a diagnosable eating disorder, but the emotions triggered by the loss influenced their eating.

Emotional eating isn't limited to the U.S. In England, a study of department store employees found that workers averaging 47 hours per week consumed significantly more sugar and saturated fat when compared with colleagues who worked 32 hours per week.[93] Another study found that daily hassles, especially in work and interpersonal situations, were associated with increased consumption of calorically dense, high fat, high sugar snacks.[94] These and dozens of other studies demonstrate the effects of emotions on eating.

IS IT EMOTIONAL EATING?

Emotional eating is defined as eating in response to unpleasant emotional arousal or to enhance an already pleasant emotional state. It's not always obvious that eating is a response to emotional arousal rather than a response to internal hunger or external cues. Controlling emotional eating would help with weight loss by decreasing unnecessary eating, but it is especially important for weight loss maintenance. Often an episode of emotional eating triggers relapse when a client had been doing well. Reducing emotional eating is also an important component in the treatment of most eating disorders.

While there is no foolproof measure, the questions below can help determine if any eating was triggered by emotions:

- Are you having a meal? (Regular meals are rarely emotional eating)
- Are you physically hungry? (If your client reports hunger pangs it's not emotional eating)
- Has anything happened that was upsetting? (Your client may be able to identify an event that occurred before having the urge to eat)
- When and where were you eating? (Eating in unusual settings, e.g., sitting alone in a parked car, may indicate emotional eating)
- Did the urge to eat come on gradually or was it sudden? (Hunger builds gradually, emotional eating is more impulsive)
- Did you eat without realizing that you were doing it? (Binge eating may occur without complete awareness)
- Did you feel guilty or ashamed after eating? (There's little or no guilt when eating a planned meal)
- Did your client report craving a specific food like pizza or ice cream? (Emotional hunger is often connected to craving a specific food and only that food will satisfy the craving; physical hunger can be satisfied by a variety of foods)
- Did your client eat until uncomfortably full? (Your client will stop eating when sated if it's physical hunger, but may continue eating if it's a response to emotions)
- Did your client eat rapidly, finishing the food in a brief period of time? (Eating quickly may result from feelings of shame and guilt)

BINGEING VS. SNACKING VS. GRAZING

It's helpful to consider different types of emotional eating. Binge eating is the most serious, but there are also less pathological patterns of emotional eating that can be categorized as either unnecessary snacking or grazing.

The DSM-5 defines a binge as:

- Eating, in a discrete period of time (e.g., within any 2-hour period), an amount of food that is definitely larger than what most people would eat in a similar period of time under similar circumstances.

- A sense of lack of control over eating during the episode (e.g., a feeling that one cannot stop eating or control what or how much one is eating).

Gail's pie and soda dinner would qualify as a binge since the amount of food is larger than what most people would eat and she reported that once she had a piece of the pie, she felt she had to eat all of it (i.e., she was unable to control her eating).

Although a "definitely larger" quantity of food consumed is part of the DSM definition of a binge, clients may report bingeing on lesser amounts of food. For example, Denise, a 24-year-old nursing student was distraught as she told me about the "binge" she'd had earlier that day. When I asked, she reported that her binge consisted of a scrambled egg, a slice of toast, and two bacon strips. While few people would see this as a large quantity of food, Denise was a rigid dieter and her breakfast was more than her diet allowed. Although the quantity of food wasn't exceptional, this episode was similar to a DSM binge because, once she started eating she couldn't stop. Often it is the lack of control, rather than the quantity of food that defines a binge. Many people will eat large quantities of food on Thanksgiving, but without the sense of being out of control, so it wouldn't be a binge.

Emotions resulting from working long hours, interpersonal conflicts or even disappointment following football games won't necessarily provoke a binge, but may cause unnecessary eating. For example, Sandy a 31-year-old, single mother of two young boys weighed 175 pounds (BMI = 31). During the day she worked as a secretary. When she got home, she made dinner, fed and bathed her kids, helped them with homework, put them to bed, and then sat down to watch TV. Before long she got up, went into the kitchen and got a snack. All day she was taking care of others, either her boss or her kids. When she finally could relax, she was lonely and feeling a little sad, so she used food to feel better. Unlike Gail, Sandy didn't consume huge quantities, nor was her eating out of control, but it was provoked by her emotions rather than physical hunger or external cues.

A third type of emotional eating, grazing, is not typically associated with strong emotional arousal, but rather it's due to boredom or a lack of stimulation. Jack was a 53-year-old CPA who weighed 189 pounds (BMI = 27). Every Wednesday afternoon, he spent several hours in the back room of a client's office working on their books. Time passed slowly. He was by himself, doing a boring task in a sterile environment so he would get up, find a vending machine and have a candy bar. Later, after doing some more work, he would talk to a secretary and help himself to some M & M's from a bowl on her desk. Eating provided stimulation and a break from the boredom he felt.

PSYCHOPATHOLOGY AND EMOTIONAL EATING

The DSM-5 definition of a binge is a feature of several diagnosable eating disorders. In addition to Binge Eating Disorder, bingeing is part of Bulimia Nervosa, and Anorexia Nervosa, Binge-eating/purging type. In order to warrant a diagnosis of Binge Eating Disorder (BED), the bingeing has to be associated with eating rapidly, feeling uncomfortably full, eating large amounts when not physically hungry, eating alone because of embarrassment, and feeling guilty, depressed or disgusted after eating. The person experiences distress over their bingeing and must binge an average of once a week for three months in order to meet the diagnostic criteria. Although it's not part of the DSM definition, for some binge eaters, the binge may have a dissociative aspect. This is a change in consciousness that is more significant than ordinary forgetfulness. For example, they may not remember all or part of their binge. Some binge eaters say that they have no memory of the binge. For example, they might report that "I started to eat and the next thing I knew I woke up from a nap."

Many clients with BED are reluctant to talk about their eating behaviors because of shame and guilt. About 25 percent of obese individuals seeking treatment meet the criteria for BED although it is less common among the general overweight population. BED may also be comorbid with depression, anxiety disorders and substance abuse. Unlike the other eating disorders, the prevalence of BED is almost equal between men and women. If you suspect your client may be a binge eater you can ask:

Have you ever experienced a sense of losing control while eating?

Have you ever felt a drive or compulsion to eat even though you knew you'd regret it afterwards?

Changes in appetite, eating, and weight that are less pronounced than a binge can be features of other diagnosable mental disorders. For example, a Major Depressive Episode can include significant weight loss or gain when not dieting, while Social Anxiety Disorder might include anxiety when eating with others. It might be fruitful to ask clients with mood or anxiety disorders about any changes in their eating habits.

It is important to recognize, and may be helpful for your clients to note, that obesity, by itself, is NOT a mental disorder. DSM-5 states:

"Finally, obesity is not included in DSM-5 as a mental disorder. Obesity (excess body fat) results from the long-term excess of energy intake relative to energy expenditure . . . However, there are robust associations between obesity and a number of mental disorders . . . and obesity may be a risk factor for the development of some mental disorders (e.g., depressive disorders)." (p. 329)

MAKING THE CONNECTION BETWEEN EMOTIONS AND EATING

There are many possible relationships between emotions and eating. For example, some people may eat when they're depressed while others lose their appetite. Likewise anxiety can trigger a binge for some while others feel that their stomach is "tied-up in knots" so they can't eat. It will help to determine the specific relationship of your client's emotions and eating.

In order to decrease emotional eating, it will be necessary to identify the relationship between emotional arousal and the urge to eat. While this relationship may appear obvious to you, the clinician, it may not register with your client. Alexithymia is defined as the difficulty in recognizing and describing one's emotions. While emotional eating is more common among women, male emotional eaters are more likely to be alexithymic.[95] They tend to describe their difficulties in terms of somatic complaints instead of emotional feelings, so they may need help identifying and discussing their emotions to make progress with their eating.

Francine, a 23-year-old binge eater, had to learn to identify her emotions so that she could see how they precipitated a binge, and then she was able to learn more effective methods of dealing with the emotion. My initial session with her was unremarkable, but during the second session I was getting some information about her family. When she described her father, tears started to form, and she looked sad. I asked how she was feeling. She replied that she was "mazzled." She used this made-up word to describe her emotional confusion. Francine knew that she was feeling something, but she wasn't able to say, "I'm sad" or "Talking about my Dad brings me down" or similar acknowledgements of sadness. Clarifying Francine's sad feelings helped her see their relationship to eating and enabled her to develop other strategies to cope with sadness.

Although many emotions could precipitate eating, depression, anxiety, anger, boredom, loneliness, and happiness are most common. The brief questionnaire that follows can help you determine which of them is most significant.

— QUESTIONNAIRE—
EMOTIONAL EATING

To get an idea of your emotional eating tendencies, look at the statements printed below. In the space next to each statement, indicate how often it occurs. Write a 1 for Never, 2 for Seldom, 3 for Sometimes, 4 for Often, and 5 for Very Often.

_____ 1. When I am feeling "down" or "blue" a little snack will lift my mood.

_____ 2. When I'm depressed I have more desire to eat.

_____ 3. If someone disappoints me I want to eat something.

_____ 4. When I am pressured or working under a deadline I have the urge to snack.

_____ 5. I eat more when I am stressed than when I am calm.

_____ 6. If I am worried or afraid of something I tend to eat.

_____ 7. Sometimes when people irritate me I want to get something to eat.

_____ 8. I have had something to eat "just to teach him/her a lesson".

_____ 9. When I get angry, eating will make me feel better.

_____ 10. I look forward to eating something when I'm bored.

_____ 11. I eat more than usual when there is nothing to do.

_____ 12. If time is passing slowly, I think about having a snack.

_____ 13. Being alone increases my appetite.

_____ 14. I eat less when other people are around than I do when I'm by myself.

_____ 15. Eating makes me feel better when I am lonely.

_____ 16. I celebrate with food when I'm in a good mood.

_____ 17. If I'm feeling really good, I don't worry about my diet.

_____ 18. When I'm happy, having a favorite snack makes me feel even better.

Although this is not a scientifically validated measure, it can offer clues to your client's eating patterns. Add the scores on items 1 - 3 to get an indication of eating while depressed. Write this total in the space below. Scores on items 4 - 6 reflect eating when anxious or stressed. Items 7 - 9 indicate eating when angry, while items 10 - 12 measure bored eating, 13 - 15 lonely eating, and 16 - 18 happy eating. Write the respective totals in the spaces below and compare these scores to see which emotion or emotions are most likely to precipitate eating. If your client scores nine or more for any emotion, you could discuss those items to help her make the connection between the emotion and unnecessary eating.

EMOTIONAL EATING SCORES

Depression (items 1 -3)   _____

Anxiety (items 4 - 6)   _____

Anger (items 7 - 9)   _____

Boredom (items 10 - 12)   _____

Loneliness (items 13 -15)   _____

Happiness (items 16 -18)   _____

The six common emotions that could trigger eating are presented below along with synonyms, a definition of the emotion, physical clues, and the thinking characteristic of the emotion. You can use the table to help your client identify his pattern of emotional eating.

Emotions That Could Trigger Eating

Emotion	Definition	Physical clues	Mental clues
Depression also: sad, down, blue, bummed	Unhappy feelings resulting from a loss of a valued person, possession, or self-esteem	Tears, slowing movement, tiredness, increased body pain, slumped posture	Thoughts of guilt, worthlessness, shame, hopelessness or pessimism about the future
Anxiety also: stress, afraid, tense, worried	A sense of uneasiness, fear or apprehensiveness about something that will happen in the future	Increased heart rate, sweating, difficulty breathing, "butterflies" in the stomach	Something awful is going to happen, may be specific ("the plane will crash") or just vague uneasiness
Anger also: mad, hostile, annoyed, irritated, pissed-off	Intense feelings resulting from a sense that you have been injured, treated unfairly, or threatened	Stiffening of the body, clenched jaw, increased blood pressure	Thoughts of striking out or attacking, getting even or revenge, thinking about the incident repeatedly
Boredom also: monotonous, dullness	Distress resulting from a lack of stimulation or repetition of uninteresting activities	Restlessness, fidgeting, yawning	Time seems to pass slowly, frequent daydreaming, easily distracted
Loneliness also: aloneness, isolation	Distress resulting from the perceived lack of satisfying social relationships	Avoidance of social situations, awkwardness around others	Thinking that you have been abandoned or rejected by others
Happiness also: joy, cheerful, elated, upbeat, euphoric	Highly pleasant state of well-being and contentment	Smiling, laughing, extra energy or drive, outgoing	Positive, optimistic thoughts, increased self-esteem

Occasionally, just identifying the emotion will be sufficient to change the behavior. For example, some clients learn to tell themselves, "I'm not hungry, I'm bored" and then find something to do to alleviate the boredom without eating.

It's also helpful for your client to learn the circumstances that contribute to emotional eating. Although there are smart phone apps that can help, the most straightforward method is old-fashioned paper and pencil. Your client can make four columns on a 3 x 5 card and record: 1) the time the eating occurred, 2) where and with whom (if others were present) it happened, 3) the type of food and approximate amount, and 4) the emotion, (or thoughts if the client can't label how she was feeling) that preceded the eating.

The Emotional Eating Record sample below shows the entries of a 53-year-old married attorney who weighed 225 pounds (BMI = 34). She was away from home for a business meeting. After dinner she was alone in her room feeling lonely and not looking forward to her meeting the next morning, so she found a vending machine and had a Snickers candy bar.

Emotional Eating Record			
Time	**Location/People**	**Food/Amount**	**Emotion (Thought)**
Tues 8:35 pm	Hotel room, alone	1 Snickers Bar	Lonely, dreading meeting tomorrow
Wed 5:50 pm	In the car, on the way home	Chocolate Milkshake	Happy the meeting is over

When you suggest keeping an emotional eating record to your client, it's quite likely that you'll encounter resistance or perhaps agreement, but then the client "forgets" to follow through. The common objections are that it's too time consuming or too difficult. In reality, it's not a difficult task, but the reluctance probably comes from guilt. Writing it down creates guilt since it provides tangible evidence that your client has been "bad" because the eating wasn't necessary.

If your client is hesitant to keep an emotional eating record, you can suggest that the goal isn't to make judgments but rather to gather data on eating habits so that you can determine his unique pattern. After a week or two, it will be possible to identify times, places, or situations that trigger emotional eating. Your client doesn't need to record all eating, just eating outside regular meals. Also, the recording should be done when he has some privacy to avoid embarrassment and the need to explain what he is doing to others. On the other hand, your client shouldn't wait until bedtime and try to remember what he ate earlier in the day.

DIETING AND EMOTIONAL EATING

Recall from Chapter 3 that chronic dieting is unlikely to result in permanent weight loss. One reason that it's unlikely to be successful is that dieting tends to *increase* emotional eating. This was demonstrated in several studies. In one study, psychologists compared restrained vs. non-restrained eaters on their responses to a frightening film or a neutral travelogue. For restrained eaters the scary film, but not the travelogue, was associated with increases in anxiety, sadness, anger, and eating. In other words, being a continual dieter increased emotional responses and resulted in more eating to cope with the emotion.[96] In an English study, women in a dieting group ate three times as much candy and nuts while being shown a frightening film (*The Shining*) compared with non-dieting women.[97]

You can help your client recognize the relationship between her diets, emotions, and eating. Gradual habit change, rather than chronic, restrictive dieting, should help her decrease emotional eating.

ALTERNATIVES TO EMOTIONAL EATING

Once you've identified the pattern of emotional eating, you can help your client manage the emotion without eating using a two-pronged cognitive and behavioral approach: 1) challenging the irrational thinking contributing to the emotion and 2) substituting other behaviors for eating.

The mental clues column on the "Emotions That Could Trigger Eating" chart (page 64) provides some of the typical thought patterns associated with the six emotions. Listen carefully as your client describes her eating and weight issues to find instances of irrational thinking. David Burns, MD, one of the pioneers of cognitive therapy, describes ten common cognitive distortions.[98] The following table lists the ten distortions, along with examples of typical weight-related irrational thoughts.

Cognitive Distortions

All-or-Nothing Thinking:

"I'm either on a diet or off my diet"; one Oreo cookie = "I've blown my diet."

Overgeneralization:

"I'll *always* be fat". The terms "always" or "never" are overgeneralizations.

Mental Filter:

Focusing on one part of a larger picture. You avoided doughnuts during coffee break; had sensible meals, yet you focus on the ice cream you ate before bedtime.

Discounting the Positive:

You walk for 30 minutes 3 times/week, but think, "It's nothing compared to people who walk every day."

Jumping to Conclusions:

Fortune telling. After eating an unplanned snack you think, "What's the use, I'll never be able to lose weight."

Magnification-Minimization:

You focus the negative experiences and minimize the positive ones. You think about your "flabby thighs" but not about your attractive facial features.

Emotional Reasoning:

Assuming that your emotions are an accurate reflection of reality. You are ashamed of your tummy, so you assume that you've done something shameful.

Should Statements (also must, ought, have to. . .):

It is reasonable to have desires, preferences and goals, but having rigid standards that you (or anyone else) should meet is irrational. For example, "I shouldn't eat any fried foods."

Labeling:

Just because you do something dumb doesn't mean you are a dummy. It is irrational to label yourself as "lazy" if you miss one exercise session.

Personalization - Blame:

It is irrational to hold yourself (or someone else) responsible for something that isn't under your (or another's) control. You have control over how much you eat, but you don't have any control over where on your body the fat will accumulate.

The second strategy for decreasing emotional eating is to develop self-soothing activities that will take the place of eating. Below are a few simple enjoyable activities that can substitute for eating.

Activities To Substitute For Eating	
• Phone, text or email a friend	• Read a magazine article
• Play with your dog or cat	• Polish your nails
• Putter in your garden	• Surf the web
• Pray or meditate	• Walk around the block
• Practice yoga or Pilates	• Soak in the tub
• Play music and dance	• Play a computer game
• Sit in the sun	• Write in your diary
• Doodle or draw	• Look at a photo album
• Ride a bike	• Work on a hobby
• Play a musical instrument	• Knit, sew, or crochet

Relaxation and mindfulness exercises[99] (see Chapter 11) can also be helpful. You may encounter resistance, typically stated as, "I don't have the time" when suggesting an activity or exercise. Many clients will feel that devoting time to themselves instead of attending to their other responsibilities is selfish or self-indulgent. You can quote the instructions that flight attendants give passengers, "Put your oxygen mask on first, then assist others" to make the point that taking care of yourself is necessary to be effective in helping others; you're not being selfish by taking a few minutes to avoid emotional eating.

ENDNOTES

91. American Psychiatric Association (2013). Diagnostic and statistical manual of mental disorders, 5th edition. Washington, DC: American Psychiatric Association.

92. Cornil, Yann & Chandon, P. (2013). From Fan to Fat? Vicarious losing increases unhealthy eating, but self-affirmation is an effective remedy. *Psychological Science, 24,* 1936–1946.

93. Wardle, J. Steptoe, A., Oliver, G. & Lipsey, Z. (2000). Stress, dietary restraint and food intake. *Journal of Psychosomatic Research, 48,* 195–202.

94. O'Connor, D. B., Jones, F., Conner, M., McMillan, B. & Ferguson, E. (2008). Effects of daily hassles and eating style on eating behavior. *Health Psychology, 27,* S20–S31.

95. Larsen, J. K., van Strien, T., Eisinga, R. & Engels, R. C. (2006). Gender differences in the association between alexithymia and emotional eating in obese individuals. *Journal of Psychosomatic Research, 60,* 237–243.

96. Schotte, D. E., Cools, J., & McNally, R. J. (1990). Film-induced negative affect triggers overeating in restrained eaters. *Journal of Abnormal Psychology, 99,* 317–320.

97. Wardle, J. & Beale, S. (1988). Control and loss of control over eating: An experimental investigation. *Journal of Abnormal Psychology, 97,* 35–40.

98. Burns, D. D. (1980). *Feeling good: The new mood therapy.* New York: William Morrow & Company.

99. Wilson, P. (1995). *Instant calm: Over 100 easy-to-use techniques for relaxing mind and body.* New York: Plume.

Williams, M., Teasdale, J., Segal, Z. & Kabat-Zinn, J. (2007). *The mindful way through depression: Freeing yourself from chronic unhappiness.* New York: Guilford.

Chapter 7

Why Are You Eating That?
— *Relationships*

Diet books and articles offer instructions on what to eat and what to avoid. The implicit assumption is that food choice and eating habits occur in a vacuum; the person just decides to eat or not to eat. Chapter 5 showed how the external cues in the physical environment affect food choices and eating habits, while Chapter 6 described the role of emotions. In this chapter, we'll explore interpersonal relationships, especially the marital dynamics that can affect eating and weight.

The effects of a relationship on one's weight can be dramatic. For example, an Ohio State study found large weight gains for women after marriage. Men didn't gain weight after marriage but had substantial gains after divorce.[100] Other times the effects of a relationship can be subtle. A study of 3,418 people over a ten-year period showed the gradual influence of spouses on eating habits.[101] There are many lifestyle changes that come with marriage that can affect weight, especially for women. For instance, women tended to gain weight after having children.[102] You can help your client identify the relationships that influence her eating and facilitate the changes necessary to insure that these relationships support, rather than impede, her efforts.

MEN, WOMEN AND WEIGHT

Being overweight may have different meanings for men and women. As a result, husbands don't always understand their wife's struggle to lose pounds, and may inadvertently make it more difficult. Traditionally, women were more likely to be valued for their physical appearance while men were valued for their accomplishments and income. Since being overweight is considered to be unattractive, women typically are more concerned about their weight.

In Western societies, there's a double standard with fatness being more salient for women than for men.[103] These gender differences start early in life. For example, a recent study found that dating someone of the "right weight" was more important to high school boys than to high school girls, meaning that high school girls were more concerned about their weight.[104] Not surprisingly, overweight adolescent girls are less likely to date compared with their average-weight peers.[105]

Gender differences in the meaning of eating and weight persist through adulthood. Traditionally, to be feminine a woman should eat salads and other healthy foods in small portions while to be masculine a man should eat unhealthy foods and drinks (e.g., chicken wings and beer) in large portions. Women tend to seek social support when they go on a diet. They may join a group program like Weight Watchers or discuss their diets with a friend. Men, on the other hand are less likely to diet, but describe their weight control efforts as "getting in shape" and do it by themselves. Snacking and calorically dense treats cause weight problems for women, while men are likely to gain weight because of large portion sizes.

There are biological differences between the sexes that can affect weight. On average, men need 12 calories to maintain each pound of their weight while women need only 11 calories for each pound, so it's easier for wives to gain. Why do women gain weight more easily? One possible explanation is that this is due to the higher proportion of body fat needed for reproduction. The result is that when a woman eats like her husband, he may maintain his weight while she'll gain.

FOOD = LOVE

Psychotherapist Geneen Roth described food compulsions:

> *Food was our love; eating was our way of being loved. Food was available when our parents weren't . . . Food was always there. Food tasted good. Food was warm when we were cold and cold when we were hot. Food became the closest thing we knew of love.*[106]

Throughout the lifespan, eating has been paired with nurturing and love. Infants are cuddled while being fed. In childhood, food often was used as a reward, like getting a special treat to celebrate a good report card or going out for ice cream after winning a soccer game. For girls, baking cookies with Mom or similar kitchen activities may be a bonding experience. Given the pairing of eating with love, it's likely that, in adulthood when a relationship is unsatisfying, food may substitute for love.

If your client's Emotional Eating Record or Emotional Eating Scale (see Chapter 6) shows eating associated with depression or loneliness, you can explore relationship issues to determine if some of the eating is a response to feeling unloved. While individual psychotherapy might be required to explore the early experience of being unloved, you can address your client's current relationship issues affecting her eating. Two relationship issues that often contribute to eating include the maintenance of equilibrium in a relationship, and sexuality.

MIXED MESSAGES

Research suggests that there's more conflict in mixed-weight couples where the wife is overweight and the husband is at a healthier weight.[107] In general, women don't need to be thin to have a happy marriage; they can be overweight as long as their BMI is less than their husband's.[108]

Weight and weight loss can have profound effects on relationships. Several studies have examined changes in relationships following bariatric surgery. For some couples, especially if the relationship was stable before surgery, weight loss can improve sexuality and the quality of the relationship. For other couples, weight loss can increase jealousy, decrease sexuality, and sometimes contributes to divorce.[109]

In a group meeting of the hospital weight management program, one of the participants, Marcy, was acutely aware of her partner's resistance to her weight loss. "Sometimes it seems as if Josh (her husband) is trying to subvert my diet," said Marcy, adding, "Tuesday he served himself a huge portion of the spaghetti I made, but when he couldn't finish it all, he told me to finish it so it wouldn't go to waste." Marcy was frustrated since Josh had been after her to lose weight. Although she'd successfully lost about 10 pounds, Josh wasn't pleased, but instead seemed to be making weight loss more difficult.

Unfortunately, Marcy's experience wasn't unique. In a survey of 200 physicians treating obesity, 90 percent reported cases where the husband sabotaged his wife's weight loss efforts.[110] In another study, Dana Powers and I found that the husbands of unsuccessful dieters were more likely to have engaged in unhelpful behaviors like bringing home sweets compared to husbands of successful dieters.[111] Occasionally, a husband might express disappointment that, even after weight loss, his wife didn't live up to his standards of beauty.

In troubled marriages, and other close relationships, an individual's weight status may become part of the dynamics in the relationship, especially if she is a frequent dieter and feels guilty about being overweight. Several prominent marriage therapists have suggested that focusing on the wife's weight struggles can maintain peace by avoiding more central issues in a distressed relationship.[112] There are several possible reasons a spouse might have mixed feelings about his partner's weight loss. For Josh, Marcy's weight loss upset the equilibrium in the relationship, and so his unhelpful behaviors were an attempt to restore the balance.

Josh was a problem drinker. Several weeks earlier he called Marcy from work to let her know that he was going to "have a beer" with a friend after work but he'd be home for dinner. Marcy was angry when he came home at 10:30 reeking of beer, but she didn't say anything that night. The next day, she didn't hold back; she let him know how angry she was. Rather than apologizing, Josh got defensive and angrily reminded her of the chocolate cake she'd had at a recent party and her numerous failures at dieting.

Marcy's weight and history of dieting failure served to maintain the equilibrium in the relationship. As long as she was overweight, overt conflict could be avoided; she couldn't criticize Josh's drinking. Whenever she mentioned his drinking, he would equate it with her dieting failures; it was his "trump card." Once she started to lose weight, he was threatened and worked to restore the equilibrium by being unhelpful while still expressing a desire for her to lose weight.

In some relationships a husband might be defensive or feel guilty about issues other than alcohol. For example, if his salary or career plans haven't met their expectations or if he's overweight and hasn't been able to lose weight, or he's neglected his responsibilities as a parent, he may attempt to minimize guilt feelings and deflect his wife's criticism by focusing on her weight issues. This dynamic may put your client in a double-bind situation. If she challenges her husband's unhelpful behaviors, he might become more defensive and escalate the conflict. On the other hand, if she suppresses her emotions, she could keep the peace, but there's evidence that it would lead to increased eating.[113]

Even in healthy relationships, weight loss can create problems. The successful partner may prod her reluctant partner to change his eating habits. In a recent study of communication after weight loss the authors note:

> *However, since the roles had shifted in a way some non-weight-loss partners had not embraced, an imbalance was created in*

couples' relational system. These non-weight-loss partners preferred to maintain the previous lifestyle or status quo, thereby creating conflict. (p. 198)[114]

You can start to assess relationship issues by asking, "Who makes comments about your eating and weight?" and allowing your client to describe the nature and circumstances of the comments. Depending on the responses you might refer the client for marriage counseling or, if the problems are less serious, you can help your client separate weight from relationship issues. Suggestions for doing this will be described below.

WEIGHT LOSS AND SEXUALITY

A review of over 30 studies found a "robust" relationship between obesity and reduced sexual functioning, with most studies reporting improvements in sexuality as weight is lost.[115] Typically, the successful loser feels better about her body, sees herself as more attractive, and is more self-assured about her sexual desirability. Likewise, her spouse is likely to find her more appealing and communicate increased interest in sexual intimacy. This clinical observation was supported by a study of 53 recently married couples. The researchers found that a wife's perceived sexual attractiveness is positively associated with marital satisfaction for both the wife and her husband. Women who saw themselves as sexually attractive reported more frequent sex and both she and her husband reported greater sexual satisfaction.[116] With weight loss, improvements in the sexual relationship may carry over to other aspects of the relationship, further strengthening the bond between the partners.

Although weight loss improves sexual relationships for most couples, it may cause difficulty for others. Since sexuality is a sensitive topic, Klotkin et al.[117] suggest it's best to address possible problems by starting with a simple open-ended question, "Do you have any concerns about any other areas of your life we have not yet discussed?" After a long pause, you can follow-up with a more targeted question such as, "Are you experiencing any concerns in your personal or sexual life?" It's often helpful to let your client know that sexual problems are frequently associated with obesity, but they often resolve following weight loss.

If your client reports sexual problems associated with their weight or weight loss attempts, it's likely that the problems can be categorized as either weight having served as "armor" or as a "chastity belt".

Melissa was a 42-year-old nurse working in a local hospital. She was overweight when she married Ted at age 18. She weighed 185 (BMI = 29) when she joined the hospital weight management program. Initially she had some success losing eight pounds but was stuck, unable to lose more. While discussing her lack of progress, it became apparent that her weight was serving a protective function; it was a self-imposed "chastity belt".

Ted was Melissa's high school sweetheart. He was the first person she had dated, and they were married shortly after graduation. Now, 24 years later with three kids, they had settled into a comfortable, if somewhat dull routine. It was apparent that Melissa cared for Ted despite describing him as "boring." She acknowledged having fantasies about some of the doctors at the hospital and lamented that she didn't date and have sexual experiences before getting married. Despite her dissatisfaction, Melissa didn't want to do anything that would jeopardize the marriage. She thought that as long as she was heavy no one would be attracted to her, and she would be too embarrassed to take her clothes off, so her marriage would be safe.

Although Melissa's "chastity belt" was self-imposed, often it is an insecure partner who views his wife's excess weight as guaranteeing her fidelity. In these relationships, the husband may be jealous and feel that her weight loss is threatening so he may complain (e.g., "Since you've been dieting, we never have any good food in the house") or make other attempts, like Josh (Marcy's husband), to undermine her weight loss efforts.

Another sexual issue that can impede weight loss occurs when a woman who has been sexually abused feels protected from further abuse by her excess weight. Samantha, a 33-year-old vice president of a small software company, was happily married with a supportive husband. She reported that she had lost 10 - 15 pounds several times, but had been unable to keep the weight off. One possible reason for her difficulty could be traced to an incident that occurred when she was a teenager. She was taking private piano lessons at her home. One day, when her parents weren't home, her piano teacher grabbed and tried to kiss her. Fortunately, she was able to deflect his advances, but this was terrifying. She was embarrassed, afraid that she might have done something to provoke her teacher, so she didn't tell her parents. She continued her piano lessons but started to gain weight.

Weight can serve as "armor", or protection from unwanted sexual advances, in two ways. Firstly, an abused woman might feel that being overweight would make her less attractive, so she'd be less likely to elicit unwelcome attention. Secondly, with a larger body, she might feel stronger and better able to repel any unwanted sexual advances.

Even in less threatening situations weight can serve as "armor". Brenda, a 38-year-old dental hygienist, had been obese since her teen years. She participated in the weight management program and had been using the treadmill at the gym for several months, but was feeling uncomfortable as she lost weight and her body became more defined. She noticed that men were looking in her direction while she was on the treadmill. Although there was no threat involved, Brenda wasn't accustomed to the attention and felt self-conscious.

Several questions can help determine if your client uses her weight as protection. If she'd lost weight previously, you could ask a general question such as, "How did it feel to be thinner?" You can follow-up with a question like, "Was there anything scary or unpleasant about losing weight?"

FRIENDS AND FAMILY

Marriage isn't the only relationship that can affect weight. Friends, co-workers, siblings and other relatives may influence your client's attempts to lose weight. Researchers in Massachusetts studied 633 school employees participating in a two-year weight gain prevention program. Participants gained weight when family members undermined their efforts. They reported unhelpful behaviors such as he "complained about the time I spent exercising" and "brought me foods I'm trying not to eat".[118]

Meredith, a 49-year-old (195 lbs., BMI = 32) participant in my hospital-based program provides a good example of family dynamics that can affect weight loss. Her twin sister, Abby, was equally heavy so they often discussed the diets they were on, their consumption of forbidden foods, and the resulting outcomes when they stepped on their scales. Meredith did well and seemed to especially enjoy the "Aerobics for Beginners" class that was part of the program. As she was losing weight, she encouraged her sister to join the program or sign-up for an aerobics class. Abby wasn't interested and seemed jealous of her sister's success. Her negative feelings were apparent at family get-togethers when she referred to Meredith as "the aerobics queen" and made other disparaging comments.

Although some family, friends or co-workers can impede your clients' weight loss attempts, others can be helpful. The Massachusetts study found friend and coworker support for healthy eating (e.g., "complimented me on changing my eating habits") and family encouragement for physical activity were associated with weight reduction after two years. Another study also found that support from friends or family members increased weight losses.[119]

DIVORCING WEIGHT FROM RELATIONSHIP ISSUES

If there is significant conflict regarding weight issues, it may be necessary to refer your client for marriage counseling. Fortunately, there are several interventions that might be helpful for less distressed couples. The basic strategy is to have your client teach her spouse to be supportive rather than critical. He can be especially helpful if he's also trying to lose weight.[120] On the other hand, if he is unwilling or unable to be supportive, and your client is committed to the relationship, then you can help her learn to divorce weight from relationship problems. Once weight is no longer a part of the marital equilibrium or serving as a chastity belt or armor, she'll be able to make progress with weight loss.

To elicit her husband's support, your client can:

- Explain that weight loss is more difficult for women than for men.
- Ask for support when making good choices rather than criticisms when the inevitable slips occur.
- Suggest that partners engage in enjoyable physical activities together.
- Request that he enjoy his calorically dense treats outside of the house.
- Ask that he not make comments about her body or other women's bodies.

If your client's husband isn't supportive, she will need to support herself so that critical comments don't derail her efforts. You can start by reviewing some of the information in Chapter 2 so that she'll feel less shame and guilt about her weight.

Help her recognize that, as a competent adult, she has the right to determine what to eat or not eat even if she chooses unhealthy food on occasion. Help her explore her feelings when others try to control her eating. Does she get rebellious and eat more to assert her independence? Does she feel defeated and give up by consoling herself with forbidden treats?

You can help your client disengage weight from marital problems. Ask her for a specific instance of her husband's unhelpful behavior and have her suggest an assertive, non-defensive response. Here are some common scenarios with some possible responses:

He tells her what to eat and nags or makes derogatory comments if she doesn't comply:

> *I know you're concerned about my weight but nagging doesn't help. What would help is. . .*

He brings up the client's weight when they are arguing about an unrelated topic (e.g., her spending):

> *We were discussing the Visa bill. The dessert I had yesterday has nothing to do with my spending. If you want to talk about my weight, let's do it later when we're not arguing.*

He offers her a calorically dense food or encourages her to eat more:

> *I'm confused. You say you want me to lose weight but then offer me extra food.*

He encourages her to lose weight but then complains when she prepares healthy meals or goes to exercise:

> *I know its inconvenient for you, but we'll both benefit if I get healthier. I really appreciate the efforts you are making to help me lose weight.*

It may help to have her role-play the response several times with you so that she can comfortably assert herself. Improving your client's body image, regardless of her current weight will also help to protect against negative comments. Although you may encounter resistance when suggesting that she can like her body at her current weight, Chapter 9 will offer suggestions for overcoming these objections.

ENDNOTES

100. Tumin, D. & Qian, Z. (2011, August 22). Large weight gains most likely for men after divorce, women after marriage. Paper presented at the annual meeting of the American Sociological Association, Las Vegas, NV.

101. Pachucki, M. A., Jacques, P. F., & Christakis, N. A. (2011). Social network concordance in food choice among spouses, friends, and siblings. *American Journal of Public Health, 101*, 2170–2177.

102. Rauschenbach, B., Sobal, J. & Frongillo, E. A. (1995). The influence of change in marital status on weight change over one year. *Obesity Research, 3,* 319–327.
103. Millman, M. (1980). *Such a pretty face: Being fat in America.* New York: W. W. Norton.
104. Sobal J., Nicolopoulos V., & Lee J. (1995). Attitudes about overweight and dating among secondary school students. *International Journal of Obesity, 19,* 376–381.
105. Pearce, M. J., Boergers, J. & Prinstein, M. J. (2002). Adolescent obesity, overt and relational peer victimization, and romantic relationships. *Obesity Research, 10,* 386–391.
106. Roth, G. (1991). *When food is love: Exploring the relationship between eating and intimacy.* New York: Plume, p. 18.
107. Burke, T. J., Randall, A. K., Corkery, S. A.. Young, V. J. & Butler, E. A. (2012). "You're going to eat that?" Relationship processes and conflict among mixed-weight couples. *Journal of Social and Personal Relationships, 29,* 1109–1130.
108. Varney, S. (2014). *XL love: How the obesity crisis is complicating America's love life.* New York: Rodale.
109. Stunkard, A. J. & Wadden, T. A. (1992). Psychological aspects of severe obesity. *American Journal of Clinical Nutrition, 55,* 524S–532S.
110. Weisz, G. & Bucher, B. (1980). Involving husbands in the treatment of obesity-Effects on weight loss, depression and marital satisfaction. *Behavior Therapy, 11,* 643–650.
111. Powers, D. & Abramson, E. E. (1997, July). Relationship of weight loss to marital adjustment. Poster presented at the Fifth European Congress of Psychology, Dublin, Ireland.
112. Marshall, J. R. (1977). The removal of a psychosomatic symptom: Effects on the marriage. *Family Process, 16,* 1145–1160.
113. Butler, E. A., Young, V. J. & Randall, A. K. (2010). Suppressing to please, eating to cope: The effect of overweight women's emotion suppression on romantic relationships and eating. *Journal of Social and Clinical Psychology, 29,* 599–623.
114. Romo, L. K. & Dailey, R. M. (2014). Weighty dynamics: Exploring couples' perceptions of post-weight-loss interaction. *Health Communication, 29,* 193–204.
115. Kolotkin, R. L., Zunker, C. & Ostbye, T. (2012). Sexual functioning and obesity: A review. *Obesity, 20,* 2325–2333.
116. Meltzer, A. L. & McNulty, J. K. (2010). Body image and marital satisfaction: Evidence for the mediating role of sexual frequency and sexual satisfaction. *Journal of Family Psychology, 24,* 156–164.
117. Kolotkin, R. L. et al. *ibid*
118. Wang, M. L., Pbert, L. & Lemon, S. C. (2014). Influence of family, friend and coworker social support and social undermining on weight gain prevention among adults. *Obesity, 22,* 1973–1979.
119. Wing, R. R. & Jeffery, R. W. (1999). Benefits of recruiting participants with friends and increasing social support for weight loss and maintenance. *Journal of Consulting and Clinical Psychology, 67,* 132–138.
120. Gorin, A., Phelan, S., Tate, D., Sherwood, N., Jeffery, R., & Wing, R. (2005). Involving support partners in obesity treatment. *Journal of Consulting and Clinical Psychology, 73,* 341–343.

Chapter 8

Why Is It So Hard To Get Active?
– Exercise

Like most overweight individuals, your clients will tend to focus on the intake side of the energy equation. Almost all of the books and popular articles they've read deal with calories, diets, fat grams, forbidden foods and so on. When the media has focused on the expenditure side of the equation, it usually revolves around extreme examples of exercise like the TV program, *The Biggest Loser*. Watching the punishing activities the participants on this program have to endure in order to lose weight is discouraging. Your client could reasonably conclude that he doesn't have the time and resources (personal trainers and equipment) necessary to lose weight by exercising and just give up.

The view that exercising for weight loss is unrealistic finds support in more reputable media. For example, a headline in *The New York Times* proclaimed, "Diet, not exercise, is crucial to weight loss."[121] This article notes that 30 minutes of jogging, which is an unrealistic goal for most overweight people, would burn only 350 calories. The same reduction could be more easily accomplished by forgoing two cans of soda. Given this information, it's not surprising that your clients would focus on eating and ignore the exercise part of the equation.

Measuring pounds lost may not be the best way to evaluate the effects of exercise. While most exercise is not going to result in significant weight loss, it may result in fat loss. Muscle tissue is heavier but more compact than fat tissue. As your client exercises and becomes more muscular, she may lose fat and have looser fitting clothes but not see any reduction when she steps on the scale.

Thinking of exercise only in terms of caloric expenditure ignores the very real benefit it provides in long-term weight control. I routinely tell clients that for permanent weight control dieting, medication, or even surgery by itself won't work; they'll need to increase their physical activity to maintain any weight loss. A study of relapse after successful weight loss found that 90 percent of successful maintainers exercised regularly while only 34 percent of relapsers routinely exercised.[122] *Consumer Reports* magazine surveyed 8,000 successful losers (10 percent or more weight loss maintained for at least one year) and found that 81 percent of them exercised at least three times per week.[123] A review of the research on physical activity concluded that it was ". . .striking in the consistency with which activity emerged as a determinant of long-term maintenance of weight loss".[124]

THE HEALTH BENEFITS OF EXERCISE

Throughout history humans have been physically active. It's only in the last few decades that we can work while seated and have many labor saving devices that enable us to avoid moving. Over many generations, we've evolved to use our bodies so if we're not active they tend to fall apart. For example, a study of 4,500 middle-aged Scottish men followed for four years found that those who spent two or more hours sitting and watching TV had double the risk of a heart attack, while those who spent four or more hours in front of a screen were 50 per cent more likely to die of any cause regardless if they exercised or not.[125] A similar study of 71,000 women aged 50 to 79 found that, after 12 years, sitting for ten or more hours per day was associated with increased risk of coronary heart disease or stroke especially for overweight women.[126]

Exercise affects health, even for people with identical genes. A carefully controlled Finnish study compared mid-20-year-old identical male twins who had different exercise patterns. The sedentary twins had more body fat, signs of insulin resistance, and less grey matter in their brains compared with their more active twin, even though they were genetically identical and raised in the same household.[127] Going from bed to car seat to desk chair to sofa and back to bed can be hazardous to your health!

The health and psychological benefits of exercise are well established. In a classic *JAMA* study of 13,334 participants, it was demonstrated that adults who exercise regularly are healthier and live longer.[128] The World Health Organization estimates that a lack of physical activity contributes to about 17 percent of diabetes and heart disease and ten percent of breast and colon cancer.[129] More recent studies have shown that regular physical activity can reduce the risk dementia and possibly Alzheimer's disease.[130] *Newsweek* neatly summarized the health benefits of exercise, "Medical science has yet to produce a treatment that can match the benefits of moderate exercise."[131] Even if weight loss is not an issue, being physically active reduces health risks.

In this chapter, I'll review the less obvious benefits of exercise for weight loss, present the common objections to becoming more active, and offer suggestions for helping clients overcome their reluctance to being active.

THE HIDDEN BENEFITS OF EXERCISE

In addition to improved health from physical activity, there are less obvious benefits. Rather than viewing exercise only in terms of weight loss, you can offer your clients a different rationale: exercise will boost mood. Unlike weight loss, which will take weeks or months to accomplish by exercising, the positive effect on mood is usually felt within a few minutes. Your client can become active just to feel better!

Another hidden benefit of exercise is that it may *decrease* cravings for chocolate and other sweet foods. In an English study, a brisk 15-minute walk reduced the chocolate urges of regular chocolate eaters.[132] Another study reported similar results for sugary snacks.[133]

Resting metabolic rate, the energy (calories) used for bodily functions like respiration, digestion, and blood circulation, tends to decline with age so it's easier to gain weight as you get older. This decline can be at least partially offset by exercise. Maintaining muscle tissue requires more energy (six calories per pound each day) than maintaining fat tissue (two calories per pound). Since exercise increases muscle mass, your client will increase her resting metabolism as she becomes more muscular even if she doesn't get bulging biceps. As a result, she'll be using more calories even when she's not being active.

Like many dieters, you client might report that she has lost weight by dieting but then easily regained the weight, perhaps with a few additional pounds. You can explain that this might be partially due to the lack of exercise. Dieting results in fat loss but also muscle loss. This is counterproductive because your client's resting metabolism will have declined with the muscle loss, making it easier to regain weight after the diet is over. Equally important, and especially relevant for weight control, are the psychological benefits of physical activity. Many studies have demonstrated that being active improves mood, relieves stress, improves memory, increases self-esteem and may be as effective as antidepressants in alleviating depression.[134]

Marian, a 54-year-old, married participant in one of my hospital weight control groups, provides a good example of the hidden benefits of exercise. She had been sedentary for many years and was deeply skeptical about the benefits of being more active. I persuaded her to join the "Aerobics for Beginners" class that was part of our program. At the six-month follow-up I asked her what was the most beneficial component of the program. She didn't hesitate; it was the aerobics class. While the aerobics didn't burn enough calories to account for her 18-pound weight loss, the aerobics did improve her mood so that she had more motivation to modify her eating habits. Becoming more active also decreased the estrangement from her body. Instead of just loathing it because of its fat, she found that using her body made her feel good!

A clever study demonstrates how thinking about being active affects weight loss. Forty-two mostly Hispanic hotel maids were told that the work they did, (vacuuming carpets, cleaning rooms, changing bed linen, etc.) was good exercise and satisfied the Surgeon General's recommendations for an active lifestyle. A matched group of 42 hotel maids wasn't given this information. Both groups continued working without any other intervention, but at the end of four weeks the group that had been told that they were exercising lost weight, lowered blood pressure, decreased body fat, and had a lower BMI.[135] Although we can only speculate about the mechanisms involved, it's likely that, like Marian, feeling good about being active resulted in healthier eating and weight loss.

ALL THE REASONS TO AVOID ACTIVITY

Although your overweight sedentary client knows he should be more active, and may have been encouraged to exercise by his physician, you'll probably encounter resistance when you suggest that he become more active. It's likely that he views exercise as unpleasant and is discouraged because past efforts resulted in trivial or no weight loss.

Many overweight clients have lost the joy in using their bodies and have a variety of rationales for remaining sedentary. Even if you suggest walking, rather than jogging or other more strenuous activity, your client can reasonably cite discouraging statistics. For example, having a Big Mac and medium Coke would result in consuming 810 calories. It would require a ten-mile hike to offset these calories. Other frequent rationales for avoiding exercise include:

- I don't have the time
- It's too boring
- I'd just eat more anyway
- I hate to sweat
- I'm too lazy, etc. etc.

You can empathize with your client's reluctance to exercise by acknowledging that movement is more difficult with extra weight and might contribute to knee and joint pain, but then gently challenge the excuses for inactivity. For example, you could ask,

> *"You're not lazy when it's time to go to work or when you have to get up in the middle of the night because your child is sick, so why do you think you're lazy when it comes to exercise?"*

> or

> *"Sweating when it's hot or when you're nervous is unpleasant, but sweating when you exercise is good; it's tangible evidence that you're increasing your cardiovascular fitness. Besides you're just going to take a shower anyway so sweat shouldn't be a problem."*

> or

> *"I know you lead a busy life, but what's more important than your health? Since all the things you need to do are dependent on you being healthy, is there something you could give up, a TV program perhaps, to make the time for exercise?"*

> or

> *"You might eat more after exercising but that's because you'd give yourself permission to eat. Perhaps you felt you've earned it or needed a reward for being active. Could you find a reward for exercising that doesn't involve food?"*

To understand the reasons for the reluctance to exercise, it might be useful to inquire about your client's childhood experiences, before physical activity became aversive. You could ask, "What activities did you enjoy as a child?" Did you like to:

- Jump rope
- Dance
- Ride your bike
- Toss a ball with your parent(s)
- Use a hula hoop
- Play hide and seek
- Play soccer

- Do gymnastics
- Go on the swing at the playground

Once you've established that there was an enjoyable childhood activity, you can explore what happened to diminish the joy. Often clients will report they've had unpleasant experiences such as:

- Feeling self-conscious wearing form-fitting outfits (e.g., swimsuits, leotards)
- Being embarrassed or feeling uncoordinated when doing poorly at a sport
- Feeling rejected when being the last chosen to join a team
- Getting criticized by a coach or gym teacher
- Having difficulty keeping up with peers or being out-of-breath
- Being nervous at a game because spectators were watching

Remembering that there was a time when your client enjoyed being active will dispel the idea that exercise is just for other people. When he recognizes that earlier unpleasant experiences can easily be avoided, you'll be able to help him explore activities that he would enjoy.

HELPING YOUR CLIENT BECOME ACTIVE WITH N.E.A.T.

N.E.A.T. is neat; it is non-exercise activity thermogenesis, or using energy (calories) in every-day activities. When you're at the gym or jogging, that's exercise. When you're lying in bed, you're using energy to maintain bodily functions (breathing, digesting, circulating blood, etc.) that's your resting metabolic rate. N.E.A.T. is everything in between like walking, shaking hands, pushing a vacuum cleaner, chewing gum, and tapping your feet to the rhythm of a catchy tune. Even fidgeting uses energy. While increasing N.E.A.T. is unlikely to result in weight loss, over time it can help with weight loss maintenance and prevention of additional weight gain.

Compared with previous generations, most of us are engaging in less N.E.A.T. According to data reported by the Bureau of Labor Statistics, the average worker is burning 150 fewer calories on the job than his parents did. While this might seem like a trivial difference, it could represent 30 or more pounds per year. Another study found that it was even worse for stay-at-home moms. They were using 360 fewer calories per day in 2010 than they had in 1965.[136]

A recent study using devices that monitored activity and posture compared lean and obese women. They found that if the obese women adopted activity patterns similar to the lean women, they would use an additional 300 calories per day.[137] Watching TV and sitting at work or at home seems to be responsible for much of the decrease in activity.

Since your clients may have negative associations to the word "exercise" you can encourage "activity" to help your clients increase movement even if they are substantially overweight and have been sedentary. Explore their daily routines at work and home to find opportunities for movement. The table below lists some simple changes in routine that will add steps.

Increasing N.E.A.T.	
Use a cordless phone and pace while talking	Get off the bus or subway one stop earlier and walk the rest of the way
Use a restroom on a different floor	When shopping park on the far side of the lot
Take a little walk during lunch	Don't accumulate things at the foot of the stairs, make a separate trip for each item
Take the stairs instead of the elevator or escalator	Don't use the drive-up window. Get out of the car and go in
Walk your dog more frequently	Put the trash can on the far side of the room
Walk to coworker's office to discuss instead of calling or emailing them	At meetings get up to get water to drink and stand at the back for a few minutes
Walk around the room during TV commercials	Walk your children to school
At work get up from the desk every half hour to stretch	When doing household chores play fast-paced music
Wash your car more often	Plant a garden

One strategy for increasing walking is to use a pedometer or smartphone app to count steps. The novelty of getting a step count often times will arouse the curiosity of sedentary clients who are reluctant to become more active. The ultimate goal should be 7,000 or more steps daily.

A meta-analysis combining data from nine studies concluded that participants lost about a pound a week during a pedometer intervention.[138] A more recent study suggests that a Fitbit, an activity tracker that syncs with a phone or computer, can be more effective than pedometers in increasing activity. The researchers speculate that the Fitbit offers more detailed feedback and engagement than a pedometer.[139] Whether your client goes hi-tech with a digital device or uses an old fashioned pedometer, monitoring steps is likely to increase movement.

I've encouraged clients to buy pedometers or digital activity trackers for all family members and post a chart so that everyone can enter their daily step count. At the end of the week they can compute daily averages and, if a predetermined goal has been met, they can reward themselves with an enjoyable family activity that doesn't involve eating. If you have an on-going relationship, you could have your client email his daily or weekly step count. A phone call or email reminder will increase compliance. Also there are several smartphone apps that will deliver prompts to motivate your client.

STAGES OF CHANGE

For sedentary clients, the prospect of committing to a sustained exercise program may seem overwhelming. You can acknowledge your client's ambivalence, but point out that changing a habit is a process that doesn't occur overnight; it takes time. Researchers[140] identified five stages of change. You can discuss these stages with your client to see where she is in the process and help move her to the next stage. It's a good idea to have your client check with his physician to get medical clearance before starting an exercise program.

The stages are:

(1) **Precontemplation:** You are not actively thinking about changing; e.g., "What's the use of exercising, I'll always be fat."

(2) **Contemplation:** You are thinking about making a change but haven't done anything about it; e.g., "I know I should exercise but I can't because (insert excuse here)."

(3) **Preparation and Planning:** You make preliminary efforts but don't follow through; e.g. "My New Year's resolution was to exercise so I signed-up for the gym but only went once or twice."

(4) **Action:** You are making a consistent effort to change behavior; e.g., "I'll walk for 30 minutes every day during my lunch break."

(5) **Maintenance/Relapse Prevention:** The new behavior becomes a habit and any "slips" are caught early and reversed; e.g., "I missed my walks

when I was sick but now that I'm back at work I'll start again." This might require revising the original plan to address reasons that led to a lapse.

Once you've identified where your client is in the change process, you can help him move to the next stage. You may need to break the desired behaviors into smaller steps. For example, if your client is ready to move from Preparation to Action, rather than walking every day for 30 minutes, he could start with a daily 10-minute walk and then gradually increase it. It will help increase adherence by finding an activity that has a purpose. For example, instead of just taking a 10-minute walk, your client could walk the dog for 10 minutes. It also helps to monitor the behavior whether it's with an activity tracker or just a paper and pencil chart.

Your client can build in rewards for progress and involve others who will be supportive. For example, the client could ask a co-worker to walk with him for 10 minutes and plan an enjoyable activity at the end of the week if they meet their goal. If your client is civic-minded, he could volunteer with the Adopt a Highway program (www.adoptahighway.com) or participate in a charity fund raising walk.

If your client reports that on some days he "just doesn't feel like it" or that he's "too tired to exercise" you can encourage him to do his routine for a shorter period or with less intensity. Although it may be difficult to start, once he's active he'll feel better and be less tired. It's likely that after he gets started he'll do most of his routine.

When your client is in the Maintenance stage, he may still benefit from your help to prevent a relapse. You can explain the difference between a lapse (slip) and a relapse (going back to baseline behaviors). Lapses are inevitable but if they are caught early you can keep them from becoming relapses. Chronic dieters, with the typical "all or nothing" mentality will assume that their lapse proves that they've failed and further attempts to exercise will be futile. You can review the lapse to determine the cause and develop alternative methods for dealing with similar situations in the future.

There are several predictable situations that are likely to result in lapsed exercise. For example, if your client's work schedule changes, it might be a challenge to reschedule his exercise routine. Or, after a vacation or an illness it might be difficult to resume his exercise. If you can anticipate situations that could cause a lapse, then you can help your client plan strategies to minimize their impact. For example, one client who had been a regular at a local gym told me he was going to be away for three months. I encouraged him to prepay the dues at his gym so he would be committed to resuming his workouts when he came home.

PHYSICIAN HEAL THYSELF

Many people in the helping professions spend a good deal of their working day sitting. If you are a nurse, dentist, or a physical therapist you're probably on your feet for much of the day but if you're a psychotherapist or administrator you sit at work. Unfortunately, sitting is hazardous to your health even if you make a deliberate effort to exercise each day. Several studies have demonstrated increased health risks from sitting independent of regular exercise.[141] While you may not be able to change your job description, you could try to use a standing desk part of the day, or at the very least, get up from your chair and walk around your office at least once per half hour.

ENDNOTES

121. Carroll, A. E. (2015, June 18). Diet, not exercise, is crucial to weight loss. *The New York Times,* p. A3.
122. Kayman, S., Bruvold, W. & Stern, J. S. (1990). Maintenance and relapse after weight loss in women: behavioral aspects. *The American Journal of Clinical Nutrition, 52,* 800–807.
123. The truth about dieting. (2002, June). *Consumer Reports,* 26–31.
124. Pronk, N. P. & Wing, R. R. (1994). Physical activity and long-term maintenance of weight loss. *Obesity Research, 2,* p. 587.
125. Stamatakis, E., Hamer, M., & Dunstan, D. W. (2011). Screen-based entertainment time, all-cause mortality, and cardiovascular events: Population-based study with ongoing mortality and hospital events follow-up. *The Journal of the American College of Cardiology, 57,* 292–299.
126. Chomistek, A. K., Manson, J. E., Stefanick, M. L. *et al.* (2013). Relationship of sedentary behavior and physical activity to incident cardiovascular disease: Results from the Women's Health Initiative. *The Journal of the American College of Cardiology, 61,* 2346–2354.
127. Rottensteiner, M., Leskinen, T., Niskanen, E., Aaltonen, S., Mutikainen, S., Wikgren, J., Heikkla, K., Kovanen, V., Kainulainen, H., Kaprio, J., Tarkana, I. M. & Kujala, U. M. (2015). Physical activity, fitness, glucose homeostasis, and brain morphology in twins. *Medicine & Science in Sports & Exercise, 47,* 509–518.
128. Blair, S. N., Kohl, H. W., Paffenbarger, R. S., Clark, D. G., Cooper, K. H. & Gibbons, L. W. (1989). Physical fitness and all-cause mortality: A prospective study of healthy men and women, *Journal of the American Medical Association, 17,* 2395–2401.
129. Silberner, Joanne (June 7, 2010). 100 years ago, exercise was blended into daily life. www.npr.org/templates/story/story.php?storyId=127525702, Retrieved 29 July 2015.

130. Hasselbalch, S. et al. (2015, July 23). Moderate to high intensity physical exercise in patients with Alzheimer's disease. Paper presented at 2015 Alzheimer's Association International Conference, Washington, D.C.

Baker, L. et al. Aerobic exercise reduces phosphorylated tau protein in cerebrospinal fluid in older adults with mild cognitive impairment. Paper presented at 2015 Alzheimer's Association International Conference, Washington, D.C.

Liu-Ambrose, T. et al. (2015, July 23) Vascular cognitive impairment and aerobic exercise: A 6-month randomized controlled trial. Paper presented at 2015 Alzheimer's Association International Conference, Washington, D.C.

131. Kalb, C. (2003, January 20). Health for life: Get up and get moving. *Newsweek, 59*–60, 62–64.

132. Taylor, A. H. & Oliver, A. J. (2009). Acute effects of brisk walking on urges to eat chocolate, affect, and responses to a stressor and chocolate cue. An experimental study. *Appetite, 52,* 155–160.

133. Ledochowski, L., Ruedl, G., Taylor, A. H., & Kopp, M. (2015). Acute effects of brisk walking on sugary snack cravings in overweight people, affect and response to a manipulated stress situation and to a sugary snack cue: A crossover study. *PLoS One, 10:* e0119278. Doi: 10.1371/journal.pone.0119278.

134. Hoffman, B. M., Babyak, M. A., & Craighead, W. E. (2011). Exercise and pharmacotherapy in patients with major depression: One-year follow-up of the SMILE study. *Psychosomatic Medicine, 73,* 127–133.

Naci, H. & Ioannidis, J. P. A. (2013). Comparative effectiveness of exercise and drug interventions on mortality outcomes: metaepidemiological study. *BMJ, 347,* f5577.

Ossip-Klein, D. J., Doyne, E. J., Bowman, E. D., Osborn, K. M., McDougall-Wilson, I. B. & Neimeyer, R. A. (1989). Effects of running or weight lifting on self-concept in clinically depressed women. *Journal of Consulting and Clinical Psychology, 57,* 158–161.

Carson, R. E. (2012). *The brain fix: What's the matter with your gray matter.* Health Communications, Deerfield Beach, FL.

135. Crum, A. J. & Langer, E. J. (2007). Mind-set matters: Exercise and the placebo effect. *Psychological Science, 18,* 165–171.

136. Reynolds, G. (2013, February 27). What housework has to do with waistlines. *The New York Times,* http://nyti.ms/1jQFwCE, accessed August 24, 2015.

137. Johannsen, D. L., Welk, G. J., Sharp, R. L. & Flakoll, P. J. (2008). Differences in daily energy expenditure in lean and obese women: The role of posture allocation. *Obesity, 16,* 34–39.

138. Richardson, C. R., Newton, T. L., Abraham, J. J., Sen, A., Jimbo, M. & Swartz, A. M. (2008). A meta-analysis of pedometer-based walking interventions and weight loss. *Annals of Family Medicine, 6,* 69–77.

139. Cadmus-Bertram, L. A., Marcus, B. H., Patterson R. E., & Parker, B. A. (2015). Randomized trial of a Fitbit-based physical activity intervention for women. *American Journal of Preventive Medicine, 49,* 414–418.

140. Prochaska, J. O., DiClemente, C. C., & Norcross, J. C. (1992). In search of how people change. *American Psychologist, 47,* 1102–1104.

141. Katzmarzyk, P. T., et al. (2009). Sitting time and mortality from all causes, cardiovascular disease, and cancer. *Medicine and Science in Sports and Exercise, 41,* 998–1005.

Chapter 9

Body Image

Discussions of anorexia nervosa and bulimia nervosa invariably describe the body image disturbance that is a central feature of these disorders. Sufferers of anorexia see themselves as "too fat" despite their obvious emaciation. Bulimics, although they usually are at a normal weight, also see themselves as needing to lose weight. Regardless of the theoretical approach, treatment for eating disorders usually includes some attempt to improve the body image of patients. In contrast, both professional and popular discussions of obesity treatment rarely mention the body image issues of obese individuals despite the evidence that body image profoundly affects self-concept, psychological well being, and the outcome of treatment. For example, one study of a behavioral weight loss program found that participants who were most dissatisfied with their weight and shape were *less* likely to lose weight.[142]

It's important to explain to your client that hating the way she looks is not a useful weight loss strategy! This chapter will offer suggestions for you to help clients improve their body image while they work on weight loss.

OBESITY AND BODY IMAGE DISSATISFACTION

Body image is more than just the way your client thinks about her appearance and attractiveness; it's her mental representation of herself. Although it is less common among African-American women, almost all white women in the U.S. are dissatisfied with their bodies. Results from body image surveys published in *Psychology Today* magazine found that body dissatisfaction among American women doubled between 1972 and 1997.[143] This near universal unhappiness has been labeled "A normative discontent".[144]

Unfortunately for many overweight individuals the number on the scale is a major determinant of their sense of wellbeing for that day regardless of whatever else is happening in their lives. In one session, a college student told me that she had been accepted into her first choice graduate program but was still upset because that morning the scale showed that she'd gained two pounds. For these clients it will be essential to address body image issues in order to successfully deal with weight control.

Not surprisingly, obese individuals report greater dissatisfaction with their bodies compared with normal weight women but the degree of dissatisfaction isn't necessarily related to the degree of obesity. In a study of bariatric surgery patients with an average BMI of 54 there was no relationship between BMI and dissatisfaction.[145]

For many women and some men, one's looks are central in determining their sense of self. For overweight women, a poor body image can result in anything from a minor behavioral adaptation (e.g., choosing clothing to hide a large body part) to significant psychological disorders such as depression,[146] social anxiety[147] and sexual dysfunction.[148] One study of sexually active college women who were self-conscious about their bodies found that they experienced orgasms 42 percent of the time, while equally heavy but less self-conscious women reported orgasms 73 percent of the time.[149]

A counselor at a franchised weight loss program told me about some of her sessions with overweight clients. Since the program was located in San Francisco's financial district, most of the clients were highly successful career women: executives, lawyers, and CPAs. Typically they were fashionably dressed and presented an aura of self-assured competence. Yet, when they started to talk about their struggles with weight their confidence crumbled. Often, the client became tearful as she described dissatisfaction with her body. Despite her significant accomplishments and outwardly projected capability, her sense of self was undermined by poor body image.

The relationship between body image and self-concept is complicated. It's likely that dissatisfaction with an overweight body lowers self-esteem but it's also possible that individuals with a poor self-concept tend to be more preoccupied with their excess weight. Regardless of which came first, weight loss requires concentration and consistent effort to change eating and exercise habits. A poor body image with the associated self-punitive thoughts will deplete the psychological resources necessary to follow treatment recommendations for habit change. As a result, weight loss will be less likely.

Many of your clients evaluate their self-worth based on their appearance, with an emphasis on their weight. Frequently they are dissatisfied when they're unable to conform to the current standards of beauty. Clearly the popular media contributes to this discontent. In the last half century, the ideal female body has become increasingly thin. For example, compare the image of Marilyn Monroe, the reigning sex goddess of the 1950s and 1960s, with contemporary actresses. During her career, Marilyn weighed between 118-135 lbs. and at her thinnest, she had a BMI of 19.6 which is in the normal range. Or, consider popular women's magazines that announce a new diet on the cover but are filled with pictures of skinny actresses and fashion models in between the numerous advertisements for calorically dense treats and desserts. Reading these magazines can make women feel worse about their bodies and themselves.[150] In 2007 the American Psychological Association released a report detailing the negative effects of sexualized images of girls found in advertising and the media. The report shows how the pervasive media images contribute to psychological problems including eating disorders, poor self-esteem, and depression.[151]

In addition to the media and cultural forces promoting body dissatisfaction, many of your clients will have been criticized or teased about features of their body. One study of female college students found that 72 percent had been repeatedly teased, usually about their weight or facial features.[152] Even without teasing, girls who mature early may develop a negative body image because they interpret newly rounded hips and breasts as evidence that they are getting fat.

Men are less likely to express body dissatisfaction[153] and when they do, it might be with a humorous reference such as "beer belly" or "love handles." Perhaps expressing dissatisfaction is not typically seen as masculine. Media portrayals of men are less focused on their physical characteristics, although the *Psychology Today* surveys found significant increases in men's body dissatisfaction over 25 years.

BODY IMAGE AND WEIGHT LOSS GOALS

A client's body image is not always an accurate representation of the physical aspects of their body. While body image is partially dependent on height, weight, shape, and other physical characteristics, overweight people frequently overestimate their actual size. Compared with non-obese individuals, their estimates average six to 12 percent larger than their actual size. Frame size and hip circumference are better predictors of dissatisfaction than the actual number of pounds of excess weight.[154]

To help clients develop more realistic views of their bodies, I often suggest that a client's mental image of their body may not be accurate. As an example of false perceptions of the body, I'll describe the phantom limb phenomenon. People who have had an arm or leg amputated sometimes report pain or itching in the limb that's been removed; their mental representation of their body is inaccurate. In a similar fashion your client's view of her body may be distorted.

While body image is a psychological phenomenon it is partially dependent on the physical reality of your client's body. Although some aspects of her body cannot be altered, her thinking about it can be. One task of treatment will be to help your client distinguish between what is predetermined by genetics and can't be changed versus what can be changed. She may need your help in developing a realistic but accepting view of those features of her body that can't be changed.

One of the more frustrating aspects of weight control relates to the distribution of fat on the body. Recall from Chapter 1 that your client has some control over how much fat he'll have but he has NO control over where the fat will accumulate. Fat distribution is determined by genetics. Most men are genetically programmed to accumulate fat in their midsection creating an apple shape, while most women tend to have fat deposits lower in the body, in the buttocks and thighs, creating a pear shape. Understanding these genetic predispositions is important in setting weight loss goals to avoid your client's disappointment if she loses weight but is still dissatisfied with a large body part.

To help your client accept her genetically determined fat distribution, you could ask her if she is close to anyone who has a similar physique. After she has named a friend, family member, or other person, ask her opinion of that person. Typically the opinion will be unrelated to the person's physique. You can then suggest that, in the same way that she isn't judging the person based on her body, significant others in her life are unlikely to have a negative view of her because of her body.

ASSESSING BODY IMAGE

Recognize that obese clients rarely describe having a poor body image as their presenting problem. They may resist discussing this topic because they feel that the features of their body are self-evident. Since everyone can see that she's overweight your client may feel that her negative thoughts are justified. Given the critical role body image plays in the emotional life of most overweight individuals and its effects on treatment outcome, it's important to assess body image early in treatment.

While there are many questionnaires assessing body image,[155] the simplest method is to have the client look at herself in a full-length mirror for 30 seconds and then rate her level of anxiety or distress on a scale from 0 to

100. She should be instructed to do this in private and to avoid focusing on one body part but rather to view her entire body. Have her record the number and repeat this exercise during and after treatment to measure her progress.

WHY IMPROVE BODY IMAGE?

Although it may seem counter-intuitive, your client will benefit from having a positive body image. In an Australian study of 5,000 women, the researchers found ". . .the improvement of body image is likely to be associated with improved quality of life among obese individuals who binge eat, irrespective of weight loss."[156] A study of recently married couples found that, independent of their body size, wives' body images were associated with marital satisfaction for both partners.[157]

You can explain that hating the way you look is demoralizing. Recall that a negative body image is associated with depression and decreased self-esteem, both of which are likely to drain the energy required for habit change. Your client may respond,

"How can I like my body when it looks like this, and if I did like it, wouldn't I gain weight? Why would I want to lose weight if I liked my body?"

Several studies have demonstrated that when overweight women and men participated in a program to improve their body image it did not result in weight gain.[158] You can explore your client's motivation for losing weight. In addition to looking good, would she want to decrease her health risks? Play with her children or grandchildren? Not be out of breath when she walks up stairs? Wear more fashionable clothes? There are many reasons for losing weight; liking your body doesn't reduce these incentives.

Research has shown that some people who lose weight still hate their bodies. About 33 percent of obese people are dissatisfied with some other aspect of their appearance in addition to their weight[159] so after losing weight, they may change their focus from hating their fat to hating another body part. For example, instead of finding their stomach to be "gross", they might be "disgusted" by the sagging skin following weight loss or an unrelated feature such as the size of their nose or a birthmark. Hating the way you look can become a habit regardless of weight.

Poor body image may contribute to the frequent failure to maintain losses after successful treatment.[160] When the weight loss doesn't result in anticipated improvements in social life, work, or other facets of life, your client may become discouraged, abandon her efforts and start to regain weight. Treatment often produces a five to ten percent weight loss. Despite the significant reduction in health risks and improvement in appearance, the loss hasn't resulted in attaining the obese client's "ideal" weight or in decreasing the size of problematic body parts. If the client's body image issues haven't been addressed in treatment it's likely that she'll feel her efforts were futile. She may then abandon her efforts and revert to her pre-treatment eating and exercise patterns resulting in regaining the lost weight.

TRANSFORMING BODY IMAGE

To improve her body image, your client will need to become aware of her negative thoughts about her body. One study found that the average woman thinks about her body every 15 minutes.[161] These thoughts are frequent and automatic, occurring without a conscious decision to focus on the body. Since they're automatic, she's not likely to recognize when she's just disparaged her body. The first task is to help her become aware of when and where she's having these thoughts so that she can learn to substitute less punitive thinking. While clients in psychotherapy are accustomed to examining their thoughts, for some other clients "thinking about your thinking" may require an explanation. You can help them become an observer of their negative self-talk.

A good place for your client to start is to have her pay attention to her thoughts when she's by herself, in the bathroom, and in front of a mirror. After she's brushed her teeth, or combed her hair or put on makeup she can pause and recall the thoughts that she had about her body. She can also track negative thoughts in the kitchen, in front of the refrigerator or pantry, in the bedroom when undressing, or out in public. To help her become aware of thought patterns your client can use a small notebook or smartphone to make a note of her thinking about her body.

After she's monitored her thinking for several days, ask her to recall a recent time when she had a negative thought about her body. Ask:

- *What activated the thought? Where was she and what was she doing? Was she by herself or with others? If other people were present, who were they and what were they doing?*
- *What were her beliefs or interpretations of the event? What did she say to herself when she was in the situation?*

- *What were the consequences of the thought? Did she feel badly? Did she avoid or withdraw or do anything differently as a result of the thought?*

You can have your client go through this sequence for additional instances to see if a pattern emerges. You may find that there are specific situations that tend to elicit body dissatisfaction. Even if there doesn't seem to be any consistency, you can challenge any irrational assumptions she's making and help to make her aware of her disparaging thoughts so that they become less automatic.

Here are some additional suggestions to help your client improve her body image. She should:

- **Pay attention to language.** Suggest that when she describes body parts she should use neutral words like, "large", "heavy", or "round" rather than pejorative terms like "gross", "ugly", or "disgusting" or "humorous" put-downs like "bubble butt" and "thunder thighs."

- **Learn to accept compliments without self-critical modifications.** When she receives a compliment about her appearance she can say, "thanks" instead of ". . .but it would look better if my stomach wasn't so big."

- **Monitor thoughts relating to her body.** For example, does she feel bad when looking in the mirror? Trying on new clothes? When eating? Once these thoughts have been identified they can be challenged and more rational thinking encouraged.

- **Identify behaviors that are avoided because of her body image.** Does she avoid dancing, going to the beach, or having sex because she's embarrassed about her body? Does she make jokes about her body to reduce self-consciousness? Help her explore the reality of the anticipated negative consequences. You could ask, "What's the worst thing that would happen if you. . .?" and then encourage participation in activities that have been avoided.

- **Consider that "problem areas" might be determined by genetics.** Do other family members have similar body shapes? Have these family members successfully engaged in behaviors she's been avoiding despite the "inheritance" they have in common?

- **Recall and reconceptualize embarrassing or painful experiences related to body size.** For example, if she was teased about her body when she was in school, what would she say to the teaser now?

- **Identify body parts that she views favorably.** Regardless of weight, does she have a pretty smile, nice eyes, or attractive hair?

- **When she looks in the mirror and focuses on a body part that she doesn't like, she should spend an equal amount of time looking at a feature she does like.**

- **Try new body positive experiences.** While she might be reluctant to buy new clothes until she loses weight she could enhance her appearance with new shoes or accessories that she could continue to use as she loses weight.

It's helpful to recognize that changing body image requires continued effort over time. Often people who have been successful changing their eating and activity habits and lost weight still see themselves as overweight. As you proceed with treatment you may need to revisit your client's thinking to help her learn to like and appreciate her body.

ENDNOTES

142. Kiernan, M., King, A. C., Kraemer, H. C., Stefanick, M. L., & Killen, J. D. (1998). Characteristics of successful and unsuccessful dieters: An application of signal detection methodology. *Annals of Behavioral Medicine, 20,* 1–6.

143. Garner, D. M. (1997). The 1997 body image survey results. *Psychology Today*, p. 30.

144. Rodin, J., Silberstein, L. & Striegel-Moore, R. (1985). Women and weight: A normative discontent. In Sonderegger, T. B. (Ed.), *Psychology and Gender: Nebraska Symposium on Motivation.* Lincoln: University of Nebraska Press, 267–307.

145. Sarwer, D. B., Wadden, T. A., Didie, E. R. & Steinberg, C. (2000, November). Body image dissatisfaction in obese women: Is there a relationship between the degree of dissatisfaction and the degree of obesity? Paper presented at the annual meeting of the Association for the Advancement of Behavior Therapy, New Orleans, LA.

146. Noles, S. W., Cash, T. F. & Winstead. B. A. (1985). Body image, physical attractiveness, and depression. *Journal of Consulting and Clinical Psychology, 53,* 88–94.

147. Cash, T. F. & Fleming, E. C. (2002). Body image and social relations. In T. F. Cash & T. Pruzinsky (Eds.), *Body image: A handbook of theory, research, and clinical practice* (pp. 277–286). New York: Guilford.

148. Wiederman, M. W. (2002). Body image and sexual functioning. In T. F. Cash & T. Pruzinsky (Eds.), *Body image: A handbook of theory, research, and clinical practice* (pp. 47–54). New York: Guilford.

149. Hangen, J. D. & Cash, T. F. (1991, November). Body-image attitudes and sexual functioning in a college population. Paper presented at the annual meeting of the Association for Advancement of Behavior Therapy, New York.

150. Turner, S. L., Hamilton, H., Jacobs, M., Angood, L. M. & Dwyer, D. H. (1997). The influence of fashion magazines on the body image satisfaction of college women: An exploratory analysis. *Adolescence, 32,* 603–614.

151. American Psychological Association, Task Force on the Sexualization of Girls. (2007). *Report of the APA Task Force on the Sexualization of Girls.* Retrieved from http://www.apa. org/pi/women/programs/girls/report-full.pdf

152. Rieves, L. & Cash, T. F. (1996). Reported social developmental factors associated with womens' body-image attitudes. *Journal of Social Behavior and Personality, 11,* 63–78.

153. Wardle, J. & Cooke, L. (2005). The impact of obesity on psychological well-being. *Best Practice & Research Clinical Endocrinology & Metabolism, 19,* 421–440.

154. Rosen, J. C. (2002). Obesity and body image. In Fairburn, C. G. & Brownell, K. D. (Eds.). *Eating disorders and obesity: A comprehensive handbook 2nd Edition.* New York: Guilford. pp. 399–402.

155. For a list of these measures see: Sarwer, D. B. & Thompson, J. K. (2002). Obesity and body image disturbance. In Wadden, T. A. & Stunkard, A. J. (Eds.) *Handbook of obesity treatment.* New York: Guilford, pp. 447–464.

156. Mond, J. M., Rodgers, B., Hay, P. J., Darby, A., Owen, C., Baune, B. T. & Kennedy, R. L. (2007). Obesity and impairment in psychosocial functioning in women: The mediating role of eating disorder features. *Obesity, 15,* 2769–2779.

157. Meltzer, A. L. & McNulty, J. K. (2010). Body image and marital satisfaction: Evidence for the mediating role of sexual frequency and sexual satisfaction. *Journal of Family Psychology, 24,* 156–165.

158. Ramirez, E. M. & Rosen, J. C. (2001). A comparison of weight control and weight control plus body image therapy for obese men and women. *Journal of Consulting and Clinical Psychology, 69,* 440–446.

159. Rosen, J. C. (2002). Obesity and body image. In Fairburn, C. G. & Brownell, K. D. (Eds.). *Eating disorders and obesity: A comprehensive handbook 2nd Edition.* New York: Guilford. pp. 399–402.

160. Cooper, Z. & Fairburn, C. G. (2002). Cognitive-behavioral treatment of obesity. In Wadden, T. A. & Stunkard, A. J. (Eds.). *Handbook of obesity treatment.* New York: Guilford. pp. 465–479.

161. Bulik, C. M. (2012). *The woman in the mirror: How to stop confusing what you look like with who you are.* New York: Walker & Company.

Chapter 10

The Obesity Epidemic: Personal Responsibility or Toxic Environment?

Traditionally, gaining weight was seen as a failure of will power. According to this widely held view the overweight person doesn't have the strength to deny himself the pleasure of too many desirable foods, or as Oscar Wilde would have it, "I can resist anything except temptation." From this perspective, it's likely that your client sees herself as being solely responsible for her obesity; if only she had more willpower she could lose weight. In contrast there's compelling evidence that, in addition to the external cues described in Chapter 5, there are larger environmental factors that could contribute to her weight gain. Everything from urban planning and architecture to governmental policies and regulations may be at least partially responsible for weight gain. While there's little that your client can do to alter many of these variables, you can help her recognize the role that environmental forces play in her weight struggles. In doing so, she can minimize their effect and stop the self-punitive thinking that discourages habit change. This chapter will describe some aspects of our "obesogenic" environment and depict the controversies surrounding possible remedies.

Kelly Brownell, a prolific researcher in this area, has suggested that rather than viewing obesity as an individual problem requiring treatment for obese persons it should be conceptualized as a public health issue.[162] He's suggested several interventions on a population level, rather than on an individual basis, to decrease the prevalence of obesity. While they wouldn't have an immediate effect, over time these interventions are predicted to decrease the number of new cases of obesity.

Recognizing the environmental contributors to obesity is especially important if you work with minority individuals. It's well established that African-American, Hispanic, and Native American individuals are at increased risk for obesity and related medical conditions including diabetes, heart disease, and stroke. Although there is some evidence that minority populations are more likely to have less healthful diets with greater consumption of sodas and fast food, this might not result from social or cultural influences, but rather may be a function of the environment. Television and radio ads for soda and calorically dense snack foods are often targeted to minority populations. In many low-income areas there are fewer supermarkets selling healthful foods. In contrast to these "food deserts", fast food outlets and corner liquor stores are plentiful.[163]

CALORIE LABELING IN RESTAURANTS

According to a U.S. Department of Agriculture survey about a third of daily calories are consumed away from home and about half of them are from fast-food restaurants.[164] The typical McDonald's meal of a Big Mac, medium fries, and medium soda provides 1,130 calories. One intervention intended to help patrons make better choices is the posting of calories on the menus of chain restaurants. A review of the effects of calorie labeling yielded mixed results. For example, one study of 100 million Starbucks transactions found a six percent reduction in calories per transaction with calorie labeling.[165] Another study found that diners at McDonald's and KFC purchased fewer calories while those at Subway purchased more after labeling.[166] The review authors concluded that, "Even if the law does not lead to changes in consumer behavior, disclosing calories could prompt the restaurant industry to make changes".[167] They suggested that, like the surgeon general's warnings on cigarette packages, calorie labeling could be a useful first step in altering the restaurant environment to reduce overeating.

If your client regularly eats at chain restaurants, ask if she notices the calorie counts on the menu. Responding to criticism, many fast-food restaurants have added healthier options to their menus. You can ask your client to search online for the caloric values of the food at her favorite restaurants. You could have her print the menus and then work with her to find lower calorie choices. Sandy, a 40-year-old government employee, routinely had lunch at Chipotle. She checked their website and found that by substituting fajita vegetables for white rice in her burrito she could save 190 calories. Since she ate at Chipotle most weeks, this would result in painlessly avoiding over 9,000 calories per year.

SODA TAXES

The most widely discussed policy intervention is the taxation of sugar-sweetened beverages. It's been estimated that Americans consume about 50 gallons of soda per year and soda consumption has the strongest association with increased fatness in school-aged children.[168] These beverages account for between 10 and 15 percent of the calories consumed by children and adolescents.[169]

In a 1994 op-ed piece in *The New York Times*, Kelly Brownell proposed taxing sodas.[170] According to one calculation a one cent per ounce tax on sweetened beverages would prevent 2.4 million cases of diabetes, 95,000 cases of heart disease and 26,000 premature deaths over the next decade.[171] When various localities such as San Francisco and Richmond, California had ballot initiatives to implement a tax on these beverages, soft drink companies spent millions of dollars to defeat these measures arguing that they impose an unfair tax burden on lower income consumers.

In 2014, voters in Berkeley, California passed a penny-per-ounce tax on sugar-sweetened beverages but this has had minimal effect. It's likely that much of the tax was not passed on to consumers and untaxed sodas are easily obtainable in surrounding cities. A better test of the effects of taxing sodas is the Mexican soda tax passed in 2013. Analysis of preliminary data from the Mexican government and American researchers found that the substantial increase in price resulted in a 12 percent decrease in soda sales.[172]

Although the soft drink industry has been largely successful in preventing soda taxes in the U.S. the publicity surrounding the unsuccessful tax initiatives may have contributed to the 25 percent decrease in full sugar soda consumption in the last 20 years. Between 2004 and 2012 American children consumed 79 fewer calories per day from sodas, representing a four percent reduction in calories consumed, which may be partially responsible for the leveling off of obesity rates in children.[173] If your clients are concerned about their children's weight, then tell them that limiting their kid's soda consumption is the single most effective means of combating juvenile obesity.

MEDIA AND ADVERTISING

Advertisers spent about $950 million each year on TV ads for kids under 12. On average, American kids see 15 food commercials a day, mostly for sugar-sweetened beverages, cookies, sugar cereals and calorically dense snacks and deserts. In 2008 the Federal Trade Commission created voluntary guidelines for marketing foods to children but a follow-up report showed that, while TV advertising decreased, on-line and mobile advertising increased. Self-regulation by the food industry has resulted in modest nutritional improvements but some food companies have ignored the recommendations. The report also noted that the entertainment industry hasn't limited the use of cartoon characters in promoting energy dense foods and snacks.[174] Nickelodeon, a cable channel programming for children, has been criticized for failing to restrict food advertisements. Chapter 12 will provide suggestions for parents to help them navigate their children's media use.

FIGHTING FAT AT WORK

Many employers are concerned about their employees' weight since obese people tend to miss work more often, incur greater health care costs, and may be less mobile doing their job. Companies including I.B.M., Safeway, and Pitney Bowes report significant savings in healthcare costs after instituting employee wellness programs with a weight loss component. For example, Lincoln Industries, a Nebraska manufacturing company with 565 employees, instituted a comprehensive wellness program that has reduced the firm's health care costs. The company saved over two million dollars in addition to significantly reducing worker's compensation costs. The company president reported that workers are more productive, safer, and had better morale as a result of the program. In addition to quarterly checkups, the program includes free gym memberships, classes on nutrition, and healthy food choices in vending machines. Employees who meet fitness goals are awarded trips and other prizes.[175]

One simple workplace strategy for losing weight is to offer a financial incentive or "bribe" for weight loss. It's estimated that 80 percent of big companies offer financial incentives for participating in wellness programs. Often the payoffs are relatively modest, for example, four dollars for every one percent of body weight lost and kept off, but many employers report that payoffs result in significant savings in health care costs.[176] Other employers offer memberships at gyms, reduced health insurance premiums, and healthier choices at employee cafeterias.

A more controversial approach to employee wellness is to charge employees for unhealthy behaviors. In 2008 PepsiCo started charging employees 50 dollars per month if they smoked or had obesity-related medical problems. Employees could avoid the penalty if they attended classes to learn to quit smoking or lose weight. Not surprisingly the unionized employees objected and filed a complaint with the National Labor Relations Board.[177]

Workplace interventions need not be as controversial as PepsiCo's nor as comprehensive as Lincoln Industries'. In his last days in office, former New York Mayor Michael Bloomberg ordered city agencies to promote the use of stairs (e.g., putting signs on walls near elevators encouraging stair use) and designing or retrofitting buildings to make the staircase more prominent than elevators.[178] Other employers including Chevron, Apple, and Google encourage their workers to use standing desks.

ARCHITECTURE AND URBAN PLANNING

Where do your clients live? Do they live in a typical sprawling suburban neighborhood requiring them to drive to work, school, and shopping? Researchers at the University of Utah found that people who live in older, denser and pedestrian-friendly (more sidewalks, less traffic, nearby stores) neighborhoods were less likely to be overweight. On average, men weighed 10 pounds less and women six pounds less if they lived in a walkable neighborhood.[179] Unfortunately, many communities have hardly any sidewalks or bicycle lanes resulting in few children walking or biking to school.

Urban planners have started to recognize that the environment affects health. In the Fruitvale neighborhood of Oakland, California there's a "transit village" comprised of housing and businesses clustered around a BART commuter rail station. In Lakewood, Colorado an abandoned shopping mall was converted into housing, businesses, and play areas. These types of neighborhoods reduce car use and increase walking. Other communities have added playgrounds and dedicated bike lanes to provide more opportunity for physical activity.

GOVERNMENT POLICY

According to some estimates, obesity accounts for more than twenty percent of total American health care costs. Since government programs such as Medicaid pay for many of these costs the Federal Government has programs such as the Department of Agriculture's Food Guide Pyramid to encourage healthy eating. Critics point out that other governmental policies actually contribute to obesity. For example, Dairy Management, a government created nonprofit corporation, helped Domino's develop and promote a line of pizzas with 40 percent more cheese.[180] Price supports for corn help provide cheap calories from high fructose corn syrup that is used to sweeten processed foods. In contrast, there are few subsidies for fresh fruit or vegetables. According to one calculation, government agriculture subsidies are enough to pay for 19 Twinkies for every American but only one quarter of an apple.

Although the jury is still out on the effectiveness of soda taxes and calorie labeling, several other interventions have been unhelpful. In Georgia, billboards with a picture of an obese child and messages such as, "Warning: Fat Kids Become Fat Adults" were removed after a public outcry that shaming kids leads to stigma and bullying but doesn't help with weight loss. In Denmark, a surcharge was put on foods containing more than 2.3 percent fat. After one year the "fat tax" was repealed because merchants complained that their customers went to Sweden and Germany to buy butter and ice cream.

Although there's little argument that we live in an environment that makes gaining weight easy and losing it difficult, attempts to make the environment less "obesogenic" are a work in progress. They're often controversial and difficult to implement but you don't have to wait for large-scale social change. You can help your client become more aware so that she can navigate this environment to minimize weight gain.

ENDNOTES

162. Brownell, K. D. (2002). Public policy and the prevention of obesity. In C. G. Fairburn & K. D. Brownell (Eds.) *Eating disorders and obesity: A comprehensive handbook (2nd ed,),* New York: Guilford.

163. Kumanyika, S. (2012). Addressing disparities related to food intake and obesity. In Brownell, K. D. & Gold, M. S. (Eds.): *Food and addiction: A comprehensive handbook.* New York, Oxford, pp. 376–381.

164. Fleishman, C. (2013). Globesity: 10 things you didn't know were making you fat. Springville, UT: Plain Sight.

165. Bollinger, B., Leslie, P. & Sorensen, A. (2011). Calorie posting in chain restaurants. *American Economic Journal: Economic Policy, 3,* 91–128.

166. Dumanovsky, T., Huang, C. Y., Nonas, C. A., Matte, T. D., Bassett, M. T. & Silver, L. D. (2011). Changes in energy content of lunchtime purchases from fast food restaurants after introduction of calorie labeling: Cross sectional customer surveys. *BMJ, 343,* 4464.

167. Block, J. P. & Roberto, C. A. (2014) Potential benefits of calorie labeling in restaurants. *JAMA, 312,* p.888.

168. Must, A., Barish, E. E. & Bandini, L. G. (2009). Modifiable risk factors in relation to changes in BMI and fatness: What have we learned from prospective studies of school-aged children? *International Journal of Obesity, 33,* 705–715.

169. Ludwig, D. S., Peterson, K. E., & Gortmaker, S. L (2001). Relation between consumption of sugar-sweetened drinks and childhood obesity: A prospective, observational analysis. *Lancet, 357,* 505–508.

170. Brownell, K. D. (1994, December 15). Get slim with higher taxes. *The New York Times,* p. A-29.

171. Wang, C. Y., Coxson, P., Shen, Y., Goldman, L. & Bibbins-Domingo, K. (2012). A penny-per-ounce tax on sugar-sweetened beverages would cut health and cost burdens of diabetes. *Health Affairs, 31,* 199–207.

172. Sanger-Katz, M. (2015, October 13). Yes, soda taxes seem to cut soda drinking. *The New York Times,* http://nyti.ms/1NDBekm, Accessed October 17, 2015.

173. Sager-Katz, M. (2015, October 2). The decline of "big soda" *The New York Times.* http://www.nytimes.com/2015/10/04/upshot/soda-industry-struggles-as-consumer-tastes-change.html. Accessed November 11, 2015.

174. Federal Trade Commission (2012). A review of food marketing to children and adolescents: A follow-up report. Washington, DC: Federal Trade Commission

175. Martin, D. S. (2008). "Wellness" a healthy investment for company. *CNN.com,* http://www.cnn.com/2008/HEALTH/diet.fitness/07/25/fn.healthy.company/index.html, October 26, 2015.

176. Langreth, R. (2009, August 24). Healthy bribes. *Forbes,* p. 72.

177. Rosenkrantz, H. & Stanford, D. (2012, March 18). PepsiCo workers balk at 'sin tax.' *San Francisco Chronicle,* p. D-5.

178. El-Naggar, M. (2013, July 17). Next steps in Bloomberg's obesity fight: Up the stairs. *The New York Times,* http://www.nytimes.com/2013/07/18/nyregion/next-steps-in-bloombergs-obesity-fight-up-the-stairs.html, Accessed October 31, 2015.

179. Smith, K. R., Brown, B. B., Yamada, I., Kowaleski-Jones, L., Zick, C. D. & Fan, J. X. (2008). Walkability and body mass index: Density, design, and new diversity measures. *American Journal of Preventive Medicine, 35,* 237–244.

180. Moss, M. (2010, November 7). While warning about fat, U.S. pushes cheese sales. *The New York Times,* p. A-1.

Chapter 11

A Treatment Program

While there are several self-help books outlining a cognitive-behavioral approach to weight control and a therapist manual describing a week-by-week therapy program,[181] this chapter will present the components of cognitive-behavioral treatment enabling you to plan a treatment tailored to your client. In contrast to the typical diet that prescribes foods to be eaten and foods to be avoided, the cognitive-behavioral approach focuses on changing your client's thinking and her environment to make unnecessary eating less likely.

You can describe the difference between your plan and your client's previous attempts to lose weight. If he attributes his previous dieting failures to a lack of will power you can explain that will power is a limited resource that can easily be depleted (see Chapter 5).[182] Making decisions, controlling emotions, resisting impulses, staying awake when sleepy and many other daily occurrences drain will power so that when an attractive food is nearby it will be difficult to resist. If your client does succeed in resisting, that will use up some will power making it more likely that he will give in when he sees the next yummy food. Rather than trying to develop more will power, the goal of treatment is to change the environment to reduce your client's need for will power to lose weight.

TALKING ABOUT WEIGHT

For many people their weight is a sensitive topic. Recall from Chapter 1 the stigmatizing negative beliefs about obesity that are held by many people including health professionals. Depending on your relationship with your client she may feel ashamed about her weight, avoid discussing the topic, and might get defensive if you bring it up directly. Instead, you can open communication by asking, "Is it okay to talk about your weight?" You'll be distinguishing yourself from others who have made disparaging comments, jokes, or given unhelpful advice. If your client doesn't want to talk about weight you can let the subject drop without having harmed your relationship.

If your client responds with a humorous or defensive statement, you can say "I know this is a difficult topic to talk about, but I have some information that you might find useful" and then check to see if it's okay to discuss.

When you start the conversation, you'll probably find that your client, having failed at previous diets, may doubt her ability to lose weight. She may quote the oft-cited statistic that 95 percent of dieters won't lose weight, and of the few who do succeed most will regain the weight. You can explain that this data comes from a 1950s study in which participants were given a printed diet and told to go home and follow it. More recent studies of current methods of weight control have yielded much better results. For example, an eight-year study of over five thousand obese adults with Type 2 diabetes compared an intensive behavioral lifestyle intervention with a typical diabetes education and support program. The participants in the behavioral program lost an average of five percent of their starting weight and 27 percent of the participants lost more than ten percent of their starting weight.[183] While your client might be disappointed with "only" a five percent weight loss, there are significant improvements in health risks even if the loss doesn't result in the ideal physique.

You can remind your clients that weight loss outcome studies report the results of people in treatment programs. It's likely that the outcome studies underestimate overall success at weight loss because the participants wouldn't be in treatment unless they had already failed at previous attempts to lose weight on their own. Several studies suggest that many people can lose weight without participating in any program. One study of 500 randomly dialed adults found that the success rate for long-term weight loss was about 20 percent.[184] Another study of 4021 obese adults found that 63 percent tried to lose weight in the previous year and 40 percent of them lost more than five percent of their body weight.[185] A *Consumer Reports* survey found that about 13 percent of the respondents were able to maintain an average weight loss of 37 pounds for five or more years with "self-directed lifestyle changes".[186] Adding the people who lost weight on their own to those who were successful in a program would yield a figure significantly higher than the oft cited five percent success rate! Despite previous failures at dieting, if your client meets readiness prerequisites it's likely that he can lose weight.

ASSESSING READINESS

Notwithstanding advertisements for miracle diets promising easy weight loss without restricting eating or increasing exercising, permanent weight control is effortful. Even bariatric surgery isn't magic; it requires changes in eating and activity habits. Before starting to work on weight issues, it's helpful to assess readiness to change since there's no point in offering treatment to someone who is unwilling or unable to implement your suggestions. Here are some guidelines to help you determine your client's readiness:

- **Is he going through any major life transitions?** If he's moving to a new city, starting a new job, going through a divorce or recovering from surgery he may not be able to devote the attention and energy required for habit change. While major disruptions would make weight loss difficult, few clients report that they are leading perfect, trouble-free lives. The ordinary hassles of living shouldn't prevent a client from using the strategies you suggest.

- **Are there drug or alcohol problems?** Despite sincere efforts, any treatment progress may be undone following an episode of substance use. You can encourage your client to get treatment for their substance use and postpone weight loss until drug and alcohol problems have been managed.

- **Are there recurrent depressive, manic, or psychotic episodes?** Psychiatric treatment may be required before tackling weight loss. As with substance use, these mental disorders may make it difficult to consistently change eating and activity behaviors.

- **Is he willing to commit to becoming more active?** As noted in Chapter 8, physical activity is necessary for weight loss maintenance. Although a client's physical limitations may make exercise difficult or impractical, with medical advice he should be willing to find activities that he can do. A trainer at a local gym could be a useful resource.

GOAL SETTING

Your client may have fond memories of how she looked when she was 18, but that shouldn't provide the basis for her weight loss goals. The genetic, metabolic and hormonal determinants outlined in Chapter 2 may put a limit on the amount of weight loss possible. Nonetheless there's ample evidence that smaller weight losses can decrease health risks and have surprisingly positive psychological benefits.

In a Pennsylvania study, 60 obese women were asked to define their dream weight, their happy weight (not as ideal as the dream weight, but they'd be happy to achieve this weight), acceptable weight (not happy, but less than their current weight) and disappointed weight (less than current weight but they'd view the loss as unsuccessful) before their treatment started. After 48 weeks of treatment the average weight loss was 38 lbs. Almost half of the participants had losses higher than their disappointed weight. Participants attaining their disappointed weight were surprised to find that achieving this weight still had positive psychological effects. Even though they still wanted to lose more, they felt more attractive, more comfortable in social situations and had increased self-confidence. Also the authors note that participants who began with a better body image and self-esteem set more realistic weight loss goals.[187] These findings suggest that improving body image (see Chapter 9) is helpful and attaining a reasonable weight loss has unexpected benefits even if the ideal goals weren't met.

It may help to have your client reformulate her goals based on what she hopes to accomplish rather than on a specific number on the scale. Although the primary goal might be to improve her appearance you can remind her that she can improve her appearance even if she doesn't reach her ideal weight and there are other benefits to weight loss. If you probe deeper you'll find some of the other benefits. Your client might agree that she'd like to:

- Decrease her risk of diabetes, cardiovascular disease and other health problems
- Be able to walk and climb stairs without being out-of-breath
- Feel comfortable dancing, swimming or doing other activities that had been avoided
- Play with children or grandchildren
- Wear more fashionable clothes
- Resume a favorite sporting activity such as bicycling, bowling, tennis, or golf

Success could be defined as attaining any of the identified goals.

COMPONENTS OF COGNITIVE-BEHAVIORAL TREATMENT

Instead of relying on willpower to make drastic changes, cognitive-behavioral treatment involves learning specific behavioral skills, typically in small steps. Unhelpful eating and exercise behaviors are examined to determine the cues and events that lead to the behavior. Then changes in thinking and in the environment are suggested to promote weight loss.

SELF-MONITORING

The most important, and possibly essential, component is self-monitoring.[188] Recording eating and activity can be done with smartphone apps (e.g., www.myfitnesspal.com), wearable activity monitors (e.g., Fitbit), or the old fashioned pencil and 3 x 5 card similar to the Emotional Eating Record described in Chapter 6. Self-monitoring of eating requires a more comprehensive and detailed, daily recording of food intake (type and amount), along with the circumstances in which it occurs. Recall from Chapter 6 that your client may be reluctant to record her food intake or just "forget" to do it. You will need to reassure her that you won't be judging her, just collecting information. You can suggest that she try it for one day, or even one meal, to see that it isn't as difficult as she had imagined.

Recording physical activity is especially important for weight loss maintenance (see Chapter 8). If your client doesn't use a wearable activity monitor she can buy an inexpensive pedometer to count her steps or use a smartphone app such Pacer, (available from the Apple App Store or Google Play). Clients can add friends to their app to provide social support to encourage increased activity.

STIMULUS CONTROL

Another component of treatment is stimulus control, or changing the environment to make eating less likely. For example, one study found that obese individuals were more likely to have food available in locations throughout the house rather than just in their kitchen.[189] You can explain stimulus control by describing several common instances when an external stimulus prompted eating without hunger. For example, ask your client,

> *Have you ever been watching a TV program when a commercial for a dessert (e.g., chocolate chip cookies) came on, and you found yourself in the kitchen looking for a similar snack?*

> or

> *Have you ever walked by a bakery or the cookie stand in a mall, smelled the baked goods and felt the urge to buy some?*

> or

> *You've had dinner and aren't hungry, but when you visit friends who are having their dessert and offer some to you, you go ahead and indulge.*

These are examples of how visual and olfactory cues can trigger unnecessary eating. Most likely your client will be able to identify similar instances but often the external cues prompting eating are not as obvious. Remember Melody's Taco Bell afternoon burritos described in Chapter 5? As you explain stimulus control to your client, you can use Melody as an example of the need to carefully self-monitor eating. Reviewing your client's self-monitoring will usually suggest environmental changes that will reduce external cues. Here are several interventions you can suggest to your client. Consider giving these to your clients as a handout.

- Keep all food in the kitchen or pantry (no snacks in the living room, no candies in the dresser drawer, or munchies in the glove compartment in the car).
- Store calorically dense foods in opaque containers and keep them in the back of the refrigerator, freezer, or pantry.
- Serve the food onto plates in the kitchen. Don't put serving bowls or platters on the table where you'll be eating.
- Increase the effort required to snack.
- Make healthy snacks easy to get (e.g., keep apple sauce or small, washed carrots in clear wrap towards the front of the refrigerator).
- Buy calorically dense snacks and treats in single serving packages (e.g., buy ice cream sandwiches instead of one quart tubs of ice cream).
- Use salad plates instead of dinner plates when serving a meal.

EATING BEHAVIORS

Often eating is done rapidly, sometimes without awareness. You can help your client slow the pace of eating by becoming mindful of her eating behaviors. A review of 19 studies of interventions designed to increase mindfulness found significant weight loss reported in 13 of the studies.[190] Several interventions can help your client slow the pace and give full attention to the act of eating so that he will be satisfied with less food.

- Never eat standing up. When at home, do all eating sitting down either in the kitchen or dining room.
- Structure eating, such as three meals and one or two snacks per day.
- Resign from the "clean plate club." Leave a small amount of food on your plate at the end of a meal.

- Make eating a singular activity. Conversation is okay, but turn off TV, don't read, text, talk on the phone, etc.
- To slow the pace of eating and establish a sense of control, put your knife and fork down in the middle of a meal, continue conversing without eating for 60 seconds, then resume eating.
- Use the non-dominant hand to eat for part of the meal.
- Put your knife and fork down after each swallow. Pause to take a breath before resuming eating.
- During a meal, stop and focus on the taste (sweet, sour, bitter), texture (soft, crunchy, chewy) and temperature of the food.
- Brush and floss your teeth after dinner to reduce the likelihood of later snacking.

You can have your client practice some of these eating behaviors in your session. For example, you could have your client bring in a favorite food. After a brief meditation or relaxation exercise have him take a small bite, savor the food and then describe the sensations that the food provides. For example, if the food is a chocolate bar, have your client notice the color then take a small bite. Have him experience the crunch as he bites into it, then the notice the sensations as it melts on his tongue before swallowing the chocolate. In addition to the sweet taste, direct his attention to the "mouth feel" or smoothness of the chocolate. Encourage your client to do a similar exercise at home. Additional mindfulness exercises can be found in several books including, *Eating Mindfully*[191] and *The Self-Compassion Diet*.[192]

EMOTIONAL EATING

It's likely that many of your clients, even those who aren't overweight, can relate to eating in response to emotional arousal. You can use the Emotional Eating Questionnaire to help your client identify her particular pattern. Depending on the frequency and intensity of the emotional eating you may want to address the underlying emotional issues as well as the unnecessary eating. If your client has an anxiety disorder, depression, or other mental health problem and you are not equipped to treat it, make a referral to a competent psychologist or therapist. Here are some suggestions for dealing with emotional eating:

- Identify the emotion(s) most likely to trigger eating. When and where are they likely to occur?

- Plan alternative methods of dealing with the emotion, such as meditation or relaxation exercises, journaling, physical activity, or getting social support.

- Develop methods of self-nurturing. Take a warm bath, read a trashy novel, play an on-line game, play with a pet, etc.

- Do boring tasks in food-free environments. For example, study in the library or do the ironing away from the kitchen.

RESTAURANTS AND SOCIAL EVENTS

From 1977 to 2000 there was a 42 percent decrease in foods consumed at home.[193] According to the Department of Agriculture, meals at fast food and sit down restaurants accounted for 20 percent of the calories Americans consumed in the years 2005 to 2008. Eating in restaurants or at social events will present a challenge to your clients since they will be tempted by calorically dense foods while having little control over their immediate environment. Here are some strategies you can use to help your client minimize the damage from eating meals away from home.

- Plan your menu before going out to eat or to a party. Avoid all-you-can-eat buffets.

- Restaurants serve large portions. Consider sharing the entrée with your companion and ordering an extra salad.

- Ask the waiter for a "doggie bag" and divide the food into the portion you'll eat and the portion you'll take home before starting to eat.

- At cocktail parties and buffets, stand on the opposite side of the room with your back to the food table.

- At a party, carry a glass of sparking water with ice cubes while you socialize.

ADDING TECHNOLOGY TO TREATMENT

Computers and smartphones can be a useful adjunct to treatment and maybe helpful when in-person treatment isn't available. A review of 23 studies concluded that using the Internet as an adjunct was effective but the effects were inconsistent depending on the type of usage and the duration of its use.[194] Often clients are enthusiastic about apps such as myfitnesspal.com, but usage typically decreases after the novelty wears off. If your client uses weight loss apps, it's a good idea to plan on frequent follow-ups to encourage continued use of the app.

MAINTENANCE AND RELAPSE PREVENTION

Virtually all forms of obesity treatment, whether surgical, medical, or behavioral, report that a significant number of participants will regain weight after successfully completing treatment. You can use several methods to help your clients maintain their weight loss.

There's some evidence that Acceptance and Commitment Therapy (ACT), a therapy approach that integrates cognitive, behavioral change, and mindfulness concepts, can help improve long-term outcomes of treatment.[195] ACT places emphasis on private thoughts, feelings, and body sensations rather than on overt behavior. Many unhelpful thoughts and feelings, such as cravings or feeling fat, contribute to relapse but rather than trying to suppress or control them, ACT encourages tolerating these internal states. The goal is to observe from a distance but not act on these thoughts and feelings; they are transient experiences, the unpleasantness will end without having to do anything. ACT is described in more detail by Hayes et al.[196]

Before the end of treatment it's helpful to explain the difference between a lapse or slip, and a relapse. A temporary abandonment of the new eating and exercise behaviors is a lapse. Lapses are inevitable; everyone has a bad day and no one is perfect! In contrast, a relapse is when the client gives up her weight loss efforts and reverts to pre-treatment behaviors. Unfortunately a perfectly normal lapse can become a relapse but with planning you can help your client avoid this outcome. Here are several predictable situations that can cause lapses:

- **Holidays and special events:** From Halloween through Thanksgiving, Christmas, New Years, and even Super Bowl, there are many opportunities to overeat so lapses are common. Birthdays, weddings and other special occasions also present challenges. Help your client anticipate specific situations and problem-solve to help them minimize their effects.

- **Vacations:** Going on vacation typically includes freedom from usual responsibilities. This may include abandoning eating rules. If the vacation is a cruise or an all-inclusive resort, eating opulent meals may be a focus of the trip. You can encourage your client to discuss eating with his travel companion to agree on less food-centric vacations or if necessary, strategies for minimizing unnecessary eating.

- **Life changes:** Moving to a new town, getting a new job, getting sick or being in a hospital can disrupt well established habits and routines. After a period of change, it will take intensified effort to reestablish the healthier behaviors. While your client may not be able to anticipate these events, you can encourage her to call you for a "tune-up" if she finds that changes in her circumstances have resulted in a lapse.

ADDITIONAL METHODS

Treatment programs often include methods that complement cognitive-behavioral techniques. For example, several studies have found that reducing food choices either by providing portion-controlled packaged foods (e.g., Medifast) or specified menus resulted in greater weight loss than standard cognitive-behavioral treatment.[197] Dietitians might make specific recommendations such as eating a protein-rich breakfast to retain fullness throughout the day or drinking water before meals to reduce eating.[198] Sports trainers and other health professionals could also be helpful when dealing with your client's specific eating and exercise issues.

ENDNOTES

181. Abramson, E. (2006). *Body intelligence: Lose weight keep it off, and feel great about your body without dieting!* New York: McGraw-Hill.
Beck, J. S. (2008). *The Beck diet solution: Train your brain to think like a thin person.* Birmingham, AL: Oxmoor House.
Cooper, Z., Fairburn, C. G., & Hawker, D. M. (2003). *Cognitive-behavioral treatment of obesity: A clinician's guide.* New York: Guilford.

182. Baumeister, R. F. & Tierney, J. (2011). *Willpower: Rediscovering the greatest human strength.* New York: Penguin.

183. The Look AHEAD Research Group (2014). Eight-year weight losses with an intensive lifestyle intervention: The look AHEAD study. *Obesity, 22,* 5–13.

184. McGuire, M. Y., Wing, R. R. & Hill, J. O. (1999). The prevalence of weight loss maintenance among American adults. *International Journal of Obesity, 23,* 1314–1319.

185. Nicklas, J. M., Huskey, K. W., Davis, R. B. & Wee, C. C. (2012). Successful weight loss among obese U. S. adults. *American Journal of Preventive Medicine. 42,* 481–485.

186. The truth about dieting. (2002, June). *Consumer Reports,* 26–31.

187. Foster, G. D., Wadden, T. A., Vogt, R. A. & Brewer, G. (1997). What is a reasonable weight loss?: Patients' expectations and evaluations of obesity treatment outcomes. *Journal of Consulting and Clinical Psychology, 65,* 79–85.

188. Baker, R. C. & Kirschenbaum, D. S. (1993). Self-monitoring may be necessary for successful weight control. *Behavior Therapy, 24,* 377–394.

189. Emery, C. F., Olson, K. L., Lee, V. S., Habash, D. L., Nasar, J. L. & Bodine. A. (2015). Home environment and psychosocial predictors of obesity status among community-residing men and women. *International Journal of Obesity, 39,* 1401–1407.

190. Olson, K. L. & Emery, C. F. (2015). Mindfulness and weight loss: A systematic review. *Psychosomatic Medicine, 77,* 59–67.

191. Albers, S. (2003). *Eating mindfully: How to end mindless eating & enjoy a balanced relationship with food.* Oakland, CA: New Harbinger.

192. Fain, J. (2011). *The self-compassion diet: A step-by-step program to lose weight with loving-kindness.* Boulder, CO: Sounds True.

193. Johnson, N. G. (2003). Psychology and health: Research, practice, and policy. *American Psychologist, 58,* 670–677.

194. Kodama, S., Saito, K., Tanaka, S., Horikawa, C., Fujiwara, K., Hirasawa, R, Yachi, Y., Iida, K. T., Shimano, H., Ohashi, Y., Yamada, N. & Sone, H. (2012). Effect of web-based lifestyle modification on weight control: A meta-analysis. *International Journal of Obesity, 36,* 675–685.

195. Lillis, J. & Kendra, K. E. (2014). Acceptance and Commitment Therapy for weight control: Model, evidence, and future directions. *Journal of Contextual Behavioral Science, 3,* 1–7.

196. Hayes, S. C., Strosahl, K., & Wilson, K. G. (1999). Acceptance and Commitment Therapy: An experiential approach to behavior change. New York: Guilford.

197. Shikany, J. M., Thomas, A. S., Beasley, T. M., Lewis, C. E. & Allison, D. B. (2013). Randomized controlled trial of the Medifast 5 & 1 Plan for weight loss. *International Journal of Obesity, 37,* 1571–1578.

198. Dennis, E. A., Dengo, A. L., Comber, D. L., Flack, K. D., Savla, J., Davy, K. P. & Davy, B. M. (2010). Water consumption increases weight loss during a hypocaloric diet intervention in middle-aged and older adults. *Obesity, 18,* 300–307.

Chapter 12

Childhood Obesity

Childhood and adolescent obesity is a serious problem. In recent years the prevalence in the U.S. has gone from five percent to more than 17 percent although the rate has remained stable since the 2003-2004 survey.[199] The health risks associated with childhood obesity are well established. For example, one study found that obese children are twice as likely to die before age 55 compared with non-obese children.[200] A study published in *The New England Journal of Medicine* concluded that, for the first time, the current generation of children might have a shorter lifespan than their parents.[201] Given the health risks associated with childhood obesity, you may be able to help address these issues with parents who are concerned about their children's weight.

While many of the health consequences including diabetes, kidney failure, and heart disease are likely to occur later in life, the negative psychological effects are more immediate. Children as young as three attribute negative characteristics such as "lazy," "ugly," "dirty," and "stupid" to their overweight peers.[202] There are significant effects of this stigmatization. Studies of adolescents found that being teased about weight was associated with lower self-esteem, depressive symptoms, suicidal ideation, and suicide attempts.[203]

Despite the seriousness of the problem, **a review of 69 studies found that 50 percent of the parents of overweight and obese children underestimated their child's weight**.[204] When should a parent become concerned about his child's weight? How should health professionals address this topic with parents when the parents aren't acknowledging the problem?

It's not obvious when a child stops having cute baby fat and starts being overweight or obese. While the BMI for an adult isn't a perfect measure (see Chapter 1), calculating adult BMI is straightforward. Using BMI as a measure of obesity for children is not as simple because kids are still growing and they don't all develop at the same rate. One possible solution is to calculate a child's BMI and then compare the result with norms for children of the same age. This would yield a BMI percentile score for the child. Doing this manually would be quite a chore but fortunately the Centers for Disease Control (CDC) has an online calculator that will do it for you. You just need to know the child's birth date, gender, height (to the nearest eighth of an inch) and weight (to the nearest quarter pound). The calculator can be accessed at: http://nccd.cdc.gov/dnpabmi/calculator.aspx. By using BMI for age percentiles, you can help your clients decide if they should be concerned about their child's weight. Typically, the 95th or above percentile indicates obesity and 85th to 95th percentile is considered overweight.

HELPING PARENTS WALK THE WEIGHT TIGHTROPE

Parents who are concerned about their child's weight are in a difficult position. If they recognize the health risks and psychological problems caused by childhood obesity most parents will want to help their child maintain a healthy weight. They might not be aware that, even with the best intentions, they could cause their child to gain weight or possibly develop an eating disorder. When you are working with parents you will need to be careful in discussing this topic. Although the weight control advice you give can be straightforward recommendations, it requires a more nuanced judgment to assess the parent's attitude about their child's weight.

Parents often believe many of the stigmatizing myths about obesity. They may attribute their child's obesity to being "lazy" or some other personality defect and communicate disappointment and disapproval to their child. Your client may feel that their child's obesity is a poor reflection of their parenting skills and be annoyed or embarrassed by the child's appearance. The result is likely to be harsh or punitive measures like nagging, overly restricting the child's food choices, and enforced dieting. Kelly R. is an example of one of the possible unfortunate results of excessive parental involvement in their child's weight issues.

Kelly was a 230 pound 26-year-old, convalescent hospital aide who appeared mildly depressed. She had a lengthy history of struggling with her weight. She recalled that in first grade her mother, who was overweight, was concerned about Kelly's "baby fat" and forbade her to eat desserts and snacks (especially Oreos, Kelly's favorite). Over the years, Kelly's mother increased her efforts to control Kelly's eating. She put Kelly on a diet, lectured her whenever she ate forbidden foods, took her to Weight Watchers meetings, and frequently expressed dissatisfaction with Kelly's weight and eating. Kelly continued to disappoint her parents by dropping out of college, taking a job that they felt was beneath their social standing, failing to lose weight, and continuing to eat Oreos.

Kelly's eating and weight difficulties might have represented an attempt to rebel against her mother's heavy-handed tactics. Excessive parental concern about weight doesn't always result in childhood obesity; it can have a more dangerous outcome. Fear of gaining weight in childhood is a risk factor for the development of an eating disorder[205] or subclinical eating problems such as overly strict dieting, excessive exercising, and having a negative body image. Often it's a mother who, with the best of intentions, transmits her own weight concerns to her daughter resulting in problematic eating behaviors.[206] This can be exacerbated when parents have difficulty dealing with the challenges of adolescence. The inevitable conflict with a teenager may be channeled into battles over eating, weight, and appearance.

In contrast, eating disorders may result from relationships that family therapists describe as "enmeshed." Like Kelly, Debra's mom was a continual dieter. Debra, a 19-year-old college freshman who binged and purged was distant from her father. She reported that he had lost interest when Debra was in high school after she dropped out of the swimming team. In contrast, Debra was very close to her mother, telling me, "My mother is my best friend." She reported that, with one exception, she could tell her mother everything. While they shared confidences about their dating and sexual experiences, Debra didn't discuss her bulimia because she "didn't want to disappoint" her mother.

Parents are in a difficult position. If they have a laissez-faire attitude about their child's weight, the intrinsic appeal of calorically dense foods along with TV and media influences can result in obesity. Conversely, if they are over involved in their child's eating and weight they may increase the risk of obesity or an eating disorder.

HELPING PARENTS CONCERNED ABOUT THEIR CHILD'S WEIGHT

Parents who are concerned about their children's weight often use methods that are unhelpful. Unlike adults, kids are still growing so they don't need to lose weight; they just need to maintain their weight while they continue to grow. Regardless of any other intervention, parents should be discouraged from putting their child on a diet. Several studies have demonstrated that for adolescents, dieting results in weight GAIN rather than weight loss.[207] A Finnish study used identical twins to control for the influence of heredity and still found that dieting was associated with weight gain.[208] Dieting is clearly counterproductive, so when discussing food choices and exercise it's better to advocate for "healthy eating" and "getting fit" rather than "going on a diet." In addition to avoiding diets, parents should be discouraged from "playful" teasing, forbidding any food, and using dessert as a reward for finishing vegetables.

Individual therapy with the overweight child is also unlikely to be successful.[209] You can show parents how to create conditions to help their child get to a healthy weight without dieting or individual sessions with the child. There are decades of research demonstrating that family-based behavioral interventions can be effective.[210] Helping a parent of an overweight child doesn't require intensive training or sophisticated techniques. A study from 42 pediatric practices found that motivational interviewing, a communication style that includes shared decision-making and reflective listening, resulted in significantly lower BMI percentiles compared with routine care after two years.[211] These findings suggest that in primary care settings, rather than just giving admonitions and advice to parents, clinicians will be more effective if they are warm, empathic, and help the client to access their motivation to change. You can encourage parents to consider the pros and cons of changing versus not changing. *Motivational interviewing: Helping people change*[212] more fully describes this method of communicating.

Several books, including my *It's NOT Just Baby Fat: 10 Steps to Help Your Child to a Healthy Weight*,[213] offer parents practical ideas for helping overweight kids. In addition to suggesting readings you can use some of the methods described below to help your clients create a home environment that promotes healthy eating, appropriate physical activity, and a healthy body image for their child.

HEALTHY EATING

Until children go off to school, their parents have control over their child's diet. Your clients can promote healthy habits that should influence their children's eating as they are exposed to friends, school, and the larger world. Many of the suggestions for children are equally useful for parents who are trying to control their own weight. The methods described in Chapter 5 for reducing external cues without dieting, as well as the guidelines for self-monitoring and stimulus control presented in Chapter 11, will also benefit children. Here are a few more suggestions that you can offer to your client:

- Minimize fast food meals, sugary drinks, calorically dense snacks and desserts.

- Don't use treats as a reward or to soothe an upset child. Parents can celebrate a good report card or soccer victory with an extra privilege instead of ice cream.

- Encourage sit-down family meals; discourage unstructured eating and snacking on the run.

- Serve a healthy breakfast; avoid sugary cereals.

Parents should avoid critical or punitive comments when the child eats unhealthy foods or when other goals aren't met. Instead, offer recognition and praise when the child succeeds in making positive behavior changes.

Getting kids to eat vegetables can be a special challenge. It's helpful for parents to realize that their children's preference for sweets is innate; they're not just being stubborn. Kids are born liking sweet tastes (mother's milk is sweet) and have to learn to like other tastes, so it's best to start with sweeter veggies like carrots and peas rather than broccoli or asparagus. If the child refuses to try the vegetables, parents shouldn't discuss, bribe, cajole or nag the child. Instead, let the matter drop and try again at another meal. Sometimes it takes 15 or 20 repetitions before the child will try a new food. While they're waiting, parents should be sure that their child sees them eating and enjoying the vegetables. They can also have the child help prepare the veggies in the kitchen or plant them in a garden. It's unlikely that a child would refuse a food that he grew and helped prepare.

When working with parents, ask about their child's sleeping since sleep can affect eating and weight. A review of 36 publications found that short sleep is associated with childhood obesity.[214] Here are recommended guidelines you can use when discussing their child's sleep:

- **Infants (3-11 months)**: 9-12 hours at night and 1-4 naps during the day
- **Toddlers (1-3 years)**: 12-14 hours including one daytime nap
- **Preschoolers (3-5 years)**: 11-13 hours
- **School-aged (5-12 years)**: 10-11 hours
- **Teens:** 8-9 hours

Often it's hard for teens to get enough sleep since they typically stay up late while their school day may start at 8 AM. Although it's easier to establish a regular bedtime routine for younger children, parents can encourage an earlier bedtime for teens.

PHYSICAL ACTIVITY

Parents of overweight children may be ready to make changes in the child's diet but less willing to consider the child's physical activity.[215] Discussing a child's physical activity with a parent will require sensitivity because of possible defensiveness about his own sedentary behavior. Nonetheless, the best way of getting children to be active is to get the parent involved in the activity. Would Mom enjoy going on a bike ride with her child? Or, how about tossing a ball in the back yard, dancing in the living room to a disco song, or even just raking leaves? One study found that kids who have two active parents were six times more likely to be active compared with their peers who had sedentary parents.[216] You could also suggest that the whole family use pedometers, smartphones, or activity trackers to record daily step counts (see Chapter 8).

Even with parental encouragement, the overweight child may resist physical activities because of possible embarrassment. For example, playing baseball or soccer could expose her to teasing and feelings of failure if she is not able to keep up with her peers. It might be better to suggest increasing movement in daily activities like walking to school, playing with the dog outside, or helping to wash the car.

Since many obese children are sedentary and spend considerable time watching TV an intervention that might elicit less parental defensiveness is to suggest limiting TV viewing. A recent study found that children ages 8 to 18 spent an average of 4 hours, 29 minutes watching TV and 2 hours 42 minutes using the computer and playing video games.[217] It's been estimated that there are an average of 10 food advertisements per hour on children's TV programs and about a third of the ads are for candy, sweets, and soft drinks.[218] Television viewing is associated with various undesirable outcomes ranging from decreased fruit and vegetable consumption[219] to reduced life expectancy.[220] There's ample evidence demonstrating that reducing television viewing results in weight loss.[221] The American Academy of Pediatrics recommends a maximum of two hours of viewing per day.

You can start the conversation by asking if there's a TV in the child's bedroom. Having a TV in the bedroom was associated with obesity in younger children[222] and poorer dietary habits, less physical activity, fewer family meals, and poorer school performance for adolescents.[223] Unless he is bedridden with an illness there really is no reason for a child to have a TV in his bedroom! Likewise, you can suggest that computers and video games be limited to common areas of the house.

BODY IMAGE

Although toddlers like their bodies, a significant number of children, some as young as six, are dissatisfied with their bodies and are concerned about their weight.[224] For girls, the dissatisfaction increases as they get older. By the time they get to school, children are aware of the stigma attached to obesity, and often have internalized the negative view of fatness. While there are limits on what your clients can do to protect their teens from media stereotypes about obesity and peer pressures they experience at school, parents can help their younger children to develop a positive body image.

For both kids and grown ups, hating the way you look is demoralizing. How can you feel good about yourself if you hate your physical being? Not liking the way you look rarely provides motivation to change. It is depressing and saps the energy required to try new behaviors. You can help your clients promote a positive body image for their kids. Parents should:

- Focus on nice features of the child's appearance instead of commenting on their weight or heavy body parts. Does she have nice eyes, a pretty smile, or fashionable hair? Is he handsome, or strong?

- Avoid negative comments or seeking reassurance about their bodies. For example, daughters don't need to hear Mom ask, "Does this make my butt look big?"

- Develop media literacy. On occasion, parents should watch TV or other media with their child and discuss unrealistic depictions of the ideal body form.

- Discuss the changes that come with puberty. Girls, especially when they mature early, may interpret their newly rounded shape as "getting fat".

- Explain the inherited aspects of body shape and size (see Chapter 9) to help the child accept genetically determined features.

SCHOOL PROGRAMS

Kids consume between 35 to 50 percent of their daily calories at school. If you work in or consult with schools, or even if you're just a concerned parent, you can advocate for school-based programs to help prevent childhood obesity. For example, one study reported increased vegetable consumption and decreases in sweetened beverages and chips after the implementation of a statewide nutrition policy for middle schools.[225] Fortunately, school-based obesity programs don't appear to increase teasing about weight.[226] Targeted interventions on a local level can also be beneficial. School vending machines could include fruits instead of candy, and milk instead of soda. A program in Ireland significantly increased fruit and vegetable consumption by showing six short episodes in which the "Food Dudes" gain "life force" from eating fruits and vegetables (http://www.fooddudes.ie/main.html). In a study conducted in upstate New York, elementary school children were given a choice between a cookie and an apple. Apples were chosen twice as often when the apple had a sticker with a cartoon character (Elmo) on it.[227]

Michele Obama's Let's Move initiative suggests that children should get 60 minutes a day of physical activity. It's estimated that only four percent of elementary schools provide even 30 minutes per day of physical education and not all of that time is spent exercising. A review of 26 studies of school-based interventions to increase physical activity did not find significant reductions in BMI,[228] although an innovative school program, Dance for Health, resulted in significantly greater reductions in BMI when compared with the usual PE class.[229] While a CDC review concluded that there wasn't sufficient evidence to determine the effectiveness of school-based programs[230] it's clear that more needs to be done to increase children's physical activity in school.

ENDNOTES

199. Ogden, C. L., Carroll, M. D., Kit, B. K. & Flegal, K. M. (2014). Prevalence of childhood and adult obesity in the United States, 2011-2012. *JAMA, 311,* 806–814.

Ogden, C. L., Flegal, K. M., Carroll, M. D. & Johnson, C. L. (2002). Prevalence and trends in overweight among US children and adolescents, 1999-2002, *JAMA, 288,* 1728–1732.

200. Franks, P. W., Hanson, R. L., Knowler, W. C., Sievers, M. L., Bennett, P. H. & Looker, H. C. (2010). Childhood obesity, other cardiovascular risk factors, and premature death, *New England Journal of Medicine, 362,* 485–493.

201. Olshansky, S. J. et al. (2005). A potential decline in life expectancy in the United States in the 21st century, *The New England Journal of Medicine, 352,* 1138–1145.

202. Haines, J. & Neumark-Sztainer, D. (2009). Psychosocial consequence of obesity and weight bias: Implications for interventions. In Heinberg, L. J. & Thompson, J. K. (Eds.) *Obesity in youth: Causes, consequences, and cures.* Washington, DC: American Psychological Association.

203. Eisenberg, M. E., Neumark-Sztainer, D., Haines, J. & Wall, M. (2006). Weight-teasing and emotional well-being in adolescents: Longitudinal findings from project EAT. *Journal of Adolescent Health, 38,* 675–683.

204. Lundahl, A,, Kidwell, K. M. & Nelson, T. D. (2014). Parental underestimates of child weight: A meta-analysis. *Pediatrics, 133,* 689–703.

205. Killen, J. D., Taylor, C. B., Hayward, C., Farish Haydel, K., Wilson, D. M., Hammer, L., Kraemer, H., Blair-Griner, A. & Strachowski, D. (1996). Weight concerns influence the development of eating disorders: A 4-year prospective study. *Journal of Consulting and Clinical Psychology, 64,* 936–940.

206. Francis, L. A. & Birch, L. L. (2005). Maternal influences on daughters' restrained eating behavior. *Health Psychology, 24,* 548–554.

207. Stice, E., Cameron, R. P., Killen, J. D., Hayward, C. & Taylor, C. B. (1999). Naturalistic weight-reduction efforts prospectively predict growth in relative weight and onset of obesity among female adolescents. *Journal of Consulting and Clinical Psychology,* 967–974. Neumark-Sztainer, D., Wall, M., Story, M. & Standish, A. R. (2012). Dieting and unhealthy weight control behaviors during adolescence: Associations with 10-year changes in body mass index. *Journal of Adolescent Health, 50,* 80–86.

208. Pietilainen, K. H., Saarni, S. E., Kaprio, J., & Rissanen, A. (2012). Does dieting make you fat? A twin study. *International Journal of Obesity 36,* 456–464.

209. Epstein, L. H., Myers, M. D., Raynor, H. A. & Salens, B. E. (1998). Treatment of pediatric obesity. *Pediatrics, 101,* 554–570.

210. Faith, M. S. & Wrotniak, B. H. (2009). Intervention: Strategies designed to affect activity level, intake patterns, and behavior. In Heinberg, L. J. & Thompson, J. K. (Eds). *Obesity in youth: Causes, consequences, and cures.* Washington DC: American Psychological Association.

211. Nierengarten, M. B. (2015, March 30). Motivational interviewing in primary care reduces obesity. *Medscape.* http://pediatrics.aappublications.org/content/135/3, Accessed December 21, 2015.

212. Miller, W. R. & Rollnick, S. (2012). *Motivational interviewing: Helping people change, 3rd edition.* New York: Guilford.

213. Abramson, E. E. (2011). *It's NOT just babyfat!: 10 Steps to help your child to a healthy weight.* Lafayette, CA: Bodega Books. See also: Ludwig, D. (2007). *Ending the food fight.* Boston: Houghton Mifflin.

214. Patel, S. R. & Hu, F. B. (2008). Short sleep duration and weight gain: A systematic review. *Obesity, 16,* 643–653.

215. Rhee, K. E., McEachern, R. & Jelalian, E. (2014). Parent readiness to change differs for overweight child dietary and physical activity behaviors. *Journal of the Academy of Nutrition and Dietetics, 114,* 1601–1610.

216. Moore, L. L., Lombardi, D. A., White, M. J., Campbell, J. L., Oliveria, S. A. & Ellison, R. C. (1991). Influence of parents' physical activity levels on activity levels of young children. *The Journal of Pediatrics, 118,* 215–219.

217. Rideout, V. J., Foehr, U. G. & Roberts, D. F. (2010). Generation M2: Media in the lives of 8-to-18-year olds, A Kaiser Family Foundation Study. Menlo Park, CA: Kaiser Family Foundation.

218. Harrison, K. & Marske, A. (2005). Nutritional content of foods advertised during the television programs children watch most. *American Journal of Public Health, 95,* 1568–1574.

219. Boynton-Jarrett, R., Thomas, T. N., Peterson, K. E., Wiecha, J., Sobol, A. M. & Gortmaker, S. L. (2003). Impact of television viewing patterns on fruit and vegetable consumption among adolescents. *Pediatrics, 112,* 1321–1326.

220. Veerman, J. L., Healy, G. N., Cobiac, L. J., Vos, T., Winkler, E. A. H., Owen, N. & Dunstan, D. W. (2012). Television viewing time and reduced life expectancy: A life table analysis. *British Journal of Sports Medicine, 46,* 927–930.

221. Epstein, L. H., Paluch, R. A., Gordy, C. C. & Dorn, J. (2000). Decreasing sedentary behaviors in treating pediatric obesity. *Archives of Pediatric and Adolescent Medicine, 154,* 220–226.

222. Dennison, B. A., Erv, T. A. & Jenkins, P. L. (2002). Television viewing and television in bedroom associated with overweight risk among low-income preschool children. *Pediatrics, 109,* 1028–1035.

223. Barr-Anderson, D. J., van den Berg, P., Neumark-Sztainer, D. & Story, M. (2008). Characteristics associated with older adolescents who have a television in their bedrooms. *Pediatrics, 121,*718–724.

224. Smolak, L. & Levine, M. P. (2001). Body image in children. In Thompson, J. K. & Smolak, L. (Eds.), *Body image eating disorders and obesity in youth: Assessment, prevention and treatment.* Washington, DC: American Psychological Association.

225. Cullen, K. W., Watson, K. & Zakeri, I. (2008). Improvements in middle school student dietary intake after implementation of the Texas Public School Nutrition Policy. *American Journal of Public Health, 98,* 111–117.

226. Krukowski, R. A., West, D. S., Siddiqui, N. J., Bursac, Z., Phillips, M. M. & Raczynski, J. M. (2008). No change in weight-based teasing when school-based obesity policies are implemented. *Archives of Pediatric and Adolescent Medicine, 162,* 936–942.

227. Wansink, B., Just, D. R. & Payne, C. R. (2012). Can branding improve school lunches? *Archives of Pediatric and Adolescent Medicine, 166,* 967–968.

228. Dobbins, M., Husson, H., DeCorby, K. & LaRocca, L. (2013, February 28). School based physical activity programs for promoting physical activity and fitness in children and adolescents aged 6 to 18. *Cochrane Database Systematic Review,* doi: 10.1002/14651858. CD007651.pub2.

229. Flores, R. (1995). Dance for health: Improving fitness in African American and Hispanic adolescents. *Public Health Reports, 110,* 189–193.

230. CDC (2005). Public health strategies for preventing and controlling overweight and obesity in school and worksite settings. A report on recommendations of the Task Force on Community Preventive Services. *MMWR,* 54(RR-10):1–12.

Made in the USA
Columbia, SC
05 June 2021

The Most Comprehensive Weight, Diet & Body Image Resource Available

Regardless of your client's diagnosis or presenting problems, they're likely to be concerned about their weight. And that impacts treatment.

Noted expert on eating and weight disorders, Edward Abramson, PhD, has created the definitive guide to help you approach weight issues and questions clients will have. Easy to read and highly practical, you'll be able to give your clients sound advice and develop realistic plans to manage their weight and feel good about their bodies.

- How to turn the whys of eating into **treatment strategies**
- **Diets, drugs and surgeries**—what you must know
- Simple environmental **changes that decrease eating**
- Tools to assess and **improve body image**
- Tips to **make exercise easier** (and enjoyable!)

> **"If you are going to get just one book on helping clients with weight issues, get this one."**
>
> – Sheira Kahn, MFT, co-author of
> *The Erasing ED Treatment Manual*

Edward Abramson, Ph.D. is a licensed clinical psychologist, professor emeritus at California State University, instructor at UC Berkeley extension, Fellow of the Obesity Society, and former director of the Eating Disorders Center at Chico Community Hospital. He is the author of five books and more than 20 scientific studies of obesity and eating disorders, and has appeared on dozens of television and radio programs including *20/20*.

PESI
Publishing
& Media
pesipublishing.com

ISBN 9781683730286

9 781683 730286

90000 >

PUB084605 $19.9